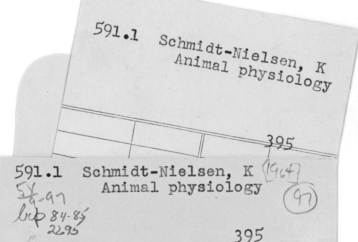

591.1   Schmidt-Nielsen, K
        Animal physiology

395

395

SAN DIEGO PUBLIC LIBRARY

LIBRARY RULES

TIME: — Books may be kept 14 days, unless dated otherwise.

RENEWALS: — Books may be renewed once at the agency where borrowed, unless on reserve. Bring book with you.

FINES: — Five cents a day will be charged for each book kept overtime.

DAMAGES: — Injury to the book from tearing, penciling, unusual soiling or other ill-usage, will be charged to the card owner. Please report to us when a mutilated book is issued to you.

CARDS — ALWAYS BRING YOUR CARD WITH YOU.

PRENTICE-HALL FOUNDATIONS OF MODERN BIOLOGY SERIES

William D. McElroy and Carl P. Swanson, Editors

NEW VOLUME

Chemical Background for the Biological Sciences, Emil H. White

SECOND EDITIONS

The Cell, Carl P. Swanson

Cell Physiology and Biochemistry, William D. McElroy

Heredity, David M. Bonner and Stanley E. Mills

Adaptation, Bruce Wallace and Adrian M. Srb

Growth and Development, Maurice Sussman

Animal Physiology, Knut Schmidt-Nielsen

Animal Diversity, Earl D. Hanson

Animal Behavior, V. G. Dethier and Eliot Stellar

The Life of the Green Plant, Arthur W. Galston

The Plant Kingdom, Harold C. Bold

Man in Nature, Marston Bates

KNUT SCHMIDT-NIELSEN   *Duke University*

Englewood Cliffs, N. J.   **PRENTICE-HALL, INC.**

Animal Physiology

SECOND EDITION

FOUNDATIONS OF MODERN BIOLOGY SERIES

ANIMAL PHYSIOLOGY, SECOND EDITION, *Knut Schmidt-Nielsen*

FOUNDATIONS OF MODERN BIOLOGY SERIES

William D. McElroy and Carl P. Swanson, Editors

Design by Walter Behnke

Drawings by Felix Cooper

Current printing (last digit):
12 11 10 9 8 7 6 5

PRENTICE-HALL INTERNATIONAL, INC., *London*
PRENTICE-HALL OF AUSTRALIA, PTY., LTD., *Sydney*
PRENTICE-HALL OF CANADA, LTD., *Toronto*
PRENTICE-HALL OF INDIA PVT. LTD., *New Delhi*
PRENTICE-HALL OF JAPAN, INC., *Tokyo*

C–03749 (p)   *C–03750 (c)*

Foundations of Modern Biology Series

PREFACE TO THE FIRST EDITION

The science of biology today is *not* the same science of fifty, twenty-five, or even ten years ago. Today's accelerated pace of research, aided by new instruments, techniques, and points of view, imparts to biology a rapidly changing character as discoveries pile one on top of the other. All of us are aware, however, that each new and important discovery is not just a mere addition to our knowledge; it also throws our established beliefs into question, and forces us constantly to reappraise and often to reshape the foundations upon which biology rests. An adequate presentation of the dynamic state of modern biology is, therefore, a formidable task and a challenge worthy of our best teachers.

The authors of this series believe that a new approach to the organization of the subject matter of biology is urgently needed to meet this challenge, an approach that introduces the student to biology as a growing, active science, and that also *permits each teacher of biology to determine the level and structure of his own course.* A single textbook cannot provide such flexibility, and it is the authors' strong conviction that these student needs and teacher prerogatives can best be met by a series of short, inexpensive, well-written, and well-illustrated books so planned as to encompass those areas of study central to an understanding of the content, state, and direction of modern biology. The FOUNDATIONS OF MODERN BIOLOGY SERIES represents the translation of these ideas into print, with each volume being complete in itself yet at the same time serving as an integral part of the series as a whole.

PREFACE TO THE SECOND EDITION

The first edition of the FOUNDATIONS OF MODERN BIOLOGY SERIES represented a marked departure from the traditions of textbook writing. The enthusiastic acceptance of the Series by teachers of biology, here and abroad, has been most heartening, and confirms our belief that there was a long-felt need for flexible teaching units based on current views and concepts. The second edition of all volumes in the Series retains the earlier flexibility, eliminates certain unnecessary overlaps of content, introduces new and relevant information, and provides more meaningful illustrative material.

The Series has also been strengthened by the inclusion of a new volume, *Chemical Background for the Biological Sciences* by Dr. Emil White. The dependence of modern biology on a sound foundation in physics and chemistry is obvious; this volume is designed to provide the necessary background in these areas.

In preparing the second edition of the Series, the authors and editors gratefully acknowledge the many constructive criticisms that have been made by hundreds of teaching biologists. Their interest and aid have made the task of writing more a pleasure than a burden.

Contents

ANIMAL PHYSIOLOGY

Food
and Energy

CHAPTER ONE

All living organisms need a supply of energy, which they must obtain from outside sources. Most plants use the energy of sunlight to build carbon dioxide from the atmosphere into sugar (by the process of *photosynthesis*) and, indirectly, into all the complicated compounds that constitute a plant. All animals, on the other hand, obtain their energy from plants, either directly by eating them, or indirectly by eating other animals that depend on plants.

Let us look at the food and energy requirements of animals, who need food for three major purposes: (1) energy and material for maintenance, (2) movements, muscle contraction, etc., and (3) growth and synthesis of body substances. The two last categories seem obvious, but the first deserves some comment. Even when an organism is at rest, many physiological processes continue. Some organs, such as the heart, work continuously, but even so-called resting organs— resting muscles, for example—continue to use nutrients and oxygen. All cells continuously expend energy, and if the process is stopped, death soon follows.

All the food requirements of animals are satisfied by the

intake of organic material of plant or animal origin. The bulk of this food consists of three major groups of compounds: *carbohydrates, fats,* and *proteins*. In addition, there is a need for a wide variety of minerals, vitamins, and various other organic compounds. The intake of food is called *feeding;* the breakdown of food into simpler compounds that can be used by the body is *digestion;* and the specific needs of an animal for certain types of food or compounds belong to the field of *nutrition*.

DIGESTION

In the most primitive way of feeding, food particles are taken into the cell for digestion (Fig. 1-1). Such *intracellular digestion* is found in protozoans

Fig. 1-1. In the ameba (A), food is taken in through the cell surface and digested in food vacuoles. The contractile vacuole is an organ of excretion. Intake of food in Paramecium (B) is restricted to one part of the cell surface, but digestion takes place in food vacuoles similar to those of the ameba. In the larger, multicellular Hydra (C), digestion begins in the coelenteron but is completed inside the cells of the body wall.

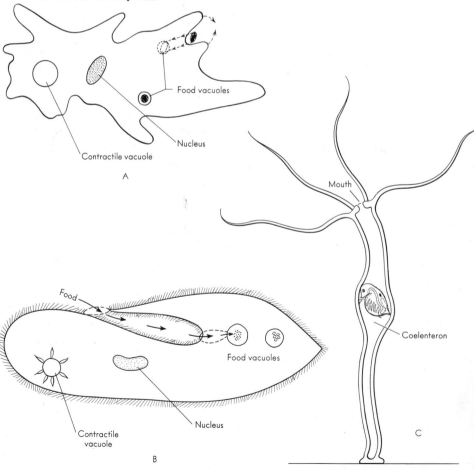

and sponges, but is also employed by more complex animals. For example, mussels filter particles out of the water, and small algae and other organisms are caught and taken into the cells of the digestive gland and digested intracellularly. In animals that feed on larger hunks of food, intracellular digestion is not possible unless the food is disintegrated beforehand. In a *Hydra,* prey that is caught by the tentacles is partly digested in the coelenteron, and the disintegrated fragments are completely digested after they have been taken into the cells. The development of a digestive tract permits a more complete *extracellular digestion.*

A few animals accomplish partial digestion before ingestion. The spider, for instance, pierces its prey with its hollow fangs and pumps digestive fluids (from the poison gland) into the victim. This liquefies the softer parts, enabling the spider to suck back the semidigested fluid. The digestion is then completed in the stomach and intestine, as it is in other animals with extracellular digestion.

Enzymatic Hydrolysis

Most food materials cannot be utilized directly by an organism until they have been broken down to simpler compounds—starches and complex sugars to simple sugars, fats to fatty acids and glycerol, and the extremely complex protein molecules to simple amino acids. This breakdown is called *hydrolysis* because water is taken up in the process. Hydrolysis is a spontaneous reaction, and as it progresses a small amount of energy is released as heat.* However, the spontaneous hydrolysis of most materials proceeds at a rate approaching zero. In general, many chemical processes can be speeded up by catalysts, and catalysts produced by living organisms are called *enzymes.* Virtually all metabolic processes—breakdown, synthesis, and certain types of chemical transfers—are catalyzed by enzymes, which, therefore, are essential to a living organism. All enzymes are protein in nature, are produced by cells, and each cell probably contains hundreds of them.

Biochemists have isolated enzymes in pure form, have studied their action, and have found that each enzyme usually acts on a single substance, the *substrate,* or on a group of closely related substances. The enzymes that act on only one particular substrate are called highly *specific.*

An enzyme can be described by the *substrate* it acts on, or by the *reaction* it catalyzes, and its activity by the *rate* of the reaction. Many factors influence the activity, and those that alter the protein of the enzyme destroy its activity. Since heat usually makes proteins coagulate, it also inactivates enzymes; on the other hand, increased temperature also speeds up chemical reactions, and a moderate increase in temperature gives an increased rate of enzymatic action. With a further temperature increase, however, the

* See the volume in this series, W. D. McElroy, *Cell Physiology and Biochemistry,* 2nd ed. (Englewood Cliffs, N. J.: Prentice-Hall, 1964).

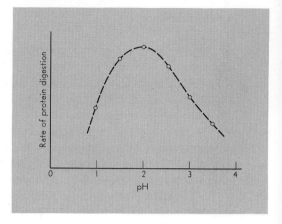

Fig. 1-2. The digestive action of the enzyme pepsin depends on the acidity, or pH. This particular enzyme has its greatest effect in acid solution about pH 2, but other enzymes have different pH optima, frequently around neutrality (pH = 7).

thermal destruction of the enzyme catches up with the increase in reaction rate, and at some temperature we will observe a maximum reaction rate, or *temperature optimum,* as we call it. Since the degree of thermal destruction increases with time, we will find a low temperature optimum in experiments that last for a long time, and a high optimum in short-lasting experiments with the same enzyme. Thus, since the temperature optimum changes with the duration of the experiment, it is not a specific characteristic of a given enzyme. Most enzymes are rapidly inactivated by temperatures above 45°C or 50°C, but a few are more resistant. One, the protein-splitting enzyme, papain, from the papaya fruit, is used as a meat tenderizer. It continues its proteolytic action at temperatures as high as 75°C, but it is inactivated by boiling.

The activity of enzymes is greatly influenced by *acidity* or *alkalinity.* Acids dissociate in water to yield hydrogen ions, H^+, and the concentration of the H^+ indicates the strength of the acid. To designate the acidity of a solution we use the symbol pH. A neutral solution has pH $= 7$; an acid solution has pH below 7 (e.g., the acid gastric juice has a pH of about 1.5); and alkaline solutions have pH above 7. This pH scale is widely used in physiology and chemistry because it gives accurate information about the hyrogen ion concentration. The pH has a profound influence on enzyme action. The curve in Fig. 1-2 shows that the action of the enzyme pepsin, from the vertebrate stomach, is greatest in a highly acid solution, about pH $= 2$, which is the *optimum pH* for pepsin. The pH optimum is characteristic for each enzyme, and many have pH optimums in neutral or slightly alkaline solutions. Excessive acidity or alkalinity causes the destruction or *denaturation* of enzymes, just as high temperature causes heat denaturation.

Digestion in Mammals

Mammals are meat eaters (carnivores), plant eaters (herbivores), or mixed-food eaters (omnivores). The main phases of digestion are alike

4

in these groups (Fig.1-3), although there are some notable variations. The *mouth and teeth* serve to some extent to tear the food to pieces. Carnivores frequently masticate the food less thoroughly than herbivores. This is related to the greater ease with which animal foods are attacked by the enzymes of digestion. Dry food cannot be easily swallowed before it has been mixed with *saliva,* secreted by the salivary glands. The saliva contains water, a small amount of salts and protein, and a digestive enzyme, *amylase,** that acts on starch. The pH optimum of amylase is neutral or slightly alkaline, which is also the normal pH range of saliva.

The *stomach* serves as a reservoir for food as well as for digestion. Glands in its wall secrete the protein-splitting, or proteolytic, enzyme *pepsin,* and hydrochloric acid in a concentration of about 0.5 per cent. The pH optimum of pepsin is about 2, and the enzyme therefore works well in the acid stomach juice. When the food comes in contact with the acid, the salivary amylase is inactivated, and starch digestion is stopped; thus the only major digestion in the stomach is proteolytic. The strong acid also inhibits bacterial growth, which otherwise would be excessive during the several hours the food stays in the stomach.

The passage of food from the stomach is controlled by a sphincter between the stomach and the upper intestine. As the sphincter relaxes, a small portion of highly acidic semi-digested food enters the upper intestine. As the acid comes in contact with the intestine, the sphincter closes firmly so that no more material leaves the stomach. The acid is

* The name is derived from the Latin word for starch, *amylum,* and the ending *-ase* which in international nomenclature designates an enzyme.

Fig. 1-3. The most important steps in vertebrate digestion. Ingested food is exposed to a succession of digestive enzymes and broken down to simple components that are absorbed in the intestine.

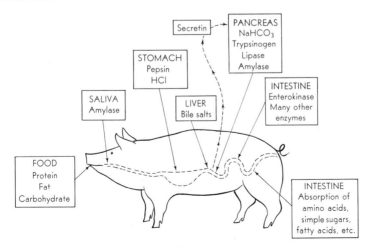

neutralized by sodium bicarbonate which is present in large quantities in the secretion from the *pancreas*. When the intestinal content has been neutralized, the sphincter relaxes again, and another portion of the acid contents of the stomach passes into the intestine. The pancreatic juice also contains enzymes; one is the powerful proteolytic enzyme *trypsin*, which has a pH optimum of about 8. Actually, trypsin is secreted as inactive *trypsinogen*. Another enzyme, *enterokinase*, which is secreted by the intestinal wall, activates the trypsinogen as the pancreatic juice enters the intestine via the pancreatic duct. Other important pancreatic enzymes are fat-digesting *lipase* and starch-digesting *amylase*, which both have pH optimums near the normal pH of the intestinal contents.

The other main digestive gland in vertebrates is the *liver*. Its secretion, the bile, contains no enzymes, but it does contain the important *bile salts*, which chemically act in the same manner as detergents. That is, they help emulsify fats, which otherwise would remain as insoluble droplets quite inaccessible to lipase action. Bile salts are essential for fat digestion, and also for the absorption of the breakdown products, the fatty acids, as well as certain other substances insoluble in water. One of these is the fat-soluble vitamin K, which is necessary for normal blood coagulation.

The *intestine* also secretes digestive juices. Its enzymes complete the hydrolysis of the breakdown products formed by the action of pepsin and trypsin on proteins, and they complete the hydrolysis of maltose, which was formed by amylase action on starch; other enzymes digest sucrose (table sugar), lactose (milk sugar), nucleic acids, and so on.

CONTROL OF THE DIGESTIVE GLANDS. The activity of the salivary glands is controlled by nerves. When food comes in contact with the mouth, a nerve reflex stimulates secretion, particularly if the food is appetizing and tasty. Mental processes play a great role in this reflex, and the smell or the mere expectation of food causes stimulation of the salivary glands and literally makes the "mouth water." Secretion of gastric juice in the stomach is also under nervous control, but, in addition, it is influenced by a substance, *gastrin*, which is formed in the wall of the stomach and during digestion circulates in the blood and causes the glands to secrete.

The pancreas has a nerve supply, but its secretion is mainly stimulated by a substance, *secretin*, that is released from the wall of the upper intestine into the blood when the acid food from the stomach enters the intestine. When the secretin reaches the pancreas via the circulatory system, pancreatic juice containing sodium bicarbonate is secreted into the intestine to neutralize the acid. In this way, the release of secretin assures that an appropriate amount of pancreatic juice is secreted. Such a "messenger" substance circulating in the blood is called a *hormone*. The secretion of bile from the liver is continuous and is not restricted to periods of digestion. The bile is stored in the gall bladder and during digestion, the gall bladder is emptied as a result of the action of another hormone, *cholecystokinin*.

Intestinal Absorption

When a final product of digestion—for example, glucose (the simple sugar formed in starch digestion)—has been formed in the intestine, it is absorbed through the intestinal wall and enters the blood. The natural tendency for dissolved substances is to migrate, or *diffuse,* from a place with a high concentration to a place with low concentration. When the concentration of glucose in the intestine is high, it may enter the blood by such diffusion, for the concentration in the blood is only 0.1 per cent. But glucose is completely absorbed from the intestine, and this cannot be explained by diffusion alone, for when the glucose molecules are completely removed, they would tend to diffuse from the blood back to the intestine.

Such movement of substances against the direction in which they tend to diffuse passively requires energy and is called *active transport,* which is defined as a movement against the concentration gradient. This transport has been compared to moving a wheelbarrow full of rocks: when the rocks are moved uphill, against their tendency to roll down, we must expend energy to push the wheelbarrow. From the laws of thermodynamics, we can calculate the amount of work needed, which depends on the steepness of the hill (the concentration gradient) and the amount of substance moved. Since the intestinal wall has the ability to transport many substances actively, these substances can be removed from the intestinal contents even though they may be present in the blood in a higher concentration. Some substances, on the other hand, penetrate passively and diffuse through the intestinal wall. This is the case with alcohol, which is absorbed and distributes itself evenly throughout all body water.

ELIMINATION. Undigested material—for example, plant fibers, the bodies of dead bacteria, epithelial cells from the intestine, etc.—are eliminated from the lower part of the intestine in the form of *feces.* The characteristic brown color of the feces is due to the excretion of bile pigments from the liver.

Digestion in Invertebrates

The invertebrates have the same main foodstuffs to digest as vertebrates, and thus they have proteases, lipases, and amylases, as well as other hydrolytic enzymes. The structure of the digestive system, however, is different, and there is a great variation in the details of the digestive processes. One characteristic difference is that invertebrates have no proteolytic enzymes that act in highly acid solution, as does the pepsin of vertebrates. It is possible that the evolution of peptic digestion is associated with the ingestion of large prey, skeletal material being more easily disintegrated in a strong acid. Pepsin and hydrochloric acid are found throughout all higher vertebrate classes from the fishes on up.

In other respects, invertebrate digestive enzymes are similar to the vertebrate digestive enzymes, although some invertebrates can digest substances indigestible to vertebrates. For example, the clothes moth can digest hair and wool, which are completely resistant to vertebrate digestion. Cellulose can be digested by many invertebrates. Some of them have cellulases, but others depend on microbes that live in their digestive tract and attack cellulose.

Symbiotic Digestion

Microbes (bacteria and protozoans) that live in an animal's digestive tract attack certain materials that cannot be hydrolyzed by the animal's enzymes and change them into substances that can be digested. A relationship between two organisms that is mutually beneficial is called *symbiosis,* and we therefore speak about *symbiotic digestion.*

CELLULOSE DIGESTION IN TERMITES. Termites feed on wood, although they do not secrete cellulase. Their intestines, however, are crowded with *protozoans* that carry out fermentation of cellulose. Each termite species carries characteristic protozoans, the newly hatched young are infected by feeding from older termites, and they will die if isolated before this occurs. It can be shown that the protozoa, and not bacteria, are responsible for the cellulose digestion. If adult termites are subjected to high oxygen concentration, the protozoans in their intestines are killed but the bacteria survive, and the termites will starve to death unless reinfected.

CELLULOSE DIGESTION IN MAMMALS. Cellulase is not produced by any vertebrate, and herbivores depend on microbes for cellulose digestion. In the horse, the fermentation takes place in an enormous pouch of the intestine, the *caecum.* In the cow and other ruminants, the true stomach is preceded by a large sac, the *rumen* (usually designated as the first of the four ruminant "stomachs"). The food, mixed with saliva, enters the rumen and undergoes heavy fermentation. The decomposition products (mostly acetic, proprionic, and butyric acids) are absorbed and utilized, while the remaining food is regurgitated, masticated, and swallowed again. It re-enters the rumen and undergoes continued fermentation. Gradually the food passes to the other parts of the stomach and is subjected to the usual digestive juices (in the cow the rumen contains no glands).

The concentration of microbes in the rumen is very high and equals that of bacterial cultures in the laboratory. Their participation in cellulose digestion is only one phase of their important function. If ammonium salts are added to the food, the bacteria use the ammonia for the synthesis of protein. These bacteria are subsequently digested. Although animals in general cannot synthesize protein from inorganic nitrogen, the symbiotic bacteria enable the cow to utilize ammonia for protein formation. This process has been employed in animal husbandry, where part of the high protein supply required by dairy cows can be replaced by cheaper ammonium salts.

In a similar fashion, inorganic sulfates are utilized by microbes for the synthesis of sulfur-containing amino acids, which are essential to life. Since the cow can utilize the bacterial protein, it is seemingly independent of the essential amino acids that are indispensable to other animals. Furthermore, certain vitamins are also synthesized by the bacteria and become available to the ruminant in the lower parts of the digestive tract. For example, the natural supply of vitamin B_{12} in ruminants is obtained entirely from micro-organisms.

The horse does not have the full advantage of microbial fermentation, for the caecum is placed in the hind end of the tract. The dead microbial bodies do not undergo complete digestion, and fermentation of the plant fibers is less complete, for there is no remastication of unfermented plant material. This can be seen from the much coarser structure of plant remains in the feces of the horse.

Rabbits and hares, which also have a large caecum for cellulose fermentation, have solved this problem in an unusual way. Two types of feces are formed, the small, firm, dark droppings that are well known, and a softer, larger, and lighter type which the rabbit does not drop but eats directly from the anus. This latter type is formed in the caecum, and the reingestion permits a more complete digestion and utilization.

WAX DIGESTION IN HONEY GUIDES. The South African honey guide, a relative of woodpeckers, is famous for its habit of guiding human beings to the nest of wild bees by a chattering and noisy behavior. When it has attracted attention and is being followed, it may guide a man to a bees' nest hundreds of yards away. It waits quietly for the nest to be plundered and then dines on the spoils. The physiological interest in this bird, which shows such a fascinating behavior, is in its diet. It seems to prefer the wax, and is known to eat pure wax as well as honeycomb. Digestion of wax is almost unique in the animal kingdom, for only the larva of the wax moth is known to accomplish it. In the honey guide, symbiotic bacteria are responsible for the digestion of the wax. Isolation of the wax-digesting enzymes from these bacteria has suggested how we can attack the waxy coating around tuberculosis bacilli that makes them particularly resistant to the defense mechanisms of the body.

NUTRITION

ENERGY SOURCES. We have seen that all sorts of organic material can be digested and utilized by animals. The bulk of the digestion products is made up of sugars (present in the food or derived from starch and cellulose digestion), fatty acids (from fat hydrolysis or cellulose fermentation), and amino acids (from protein). The oxidation of these compounds yields almost all the energy needed in the body. Since amino acids are also the basic constituents of protein, which makes up a major part of the body, they are important structural compounds as well. If they are used for energy, the amino group ($-NH_2$), containing the nitrogen, is removed from the molecule (by deamination) before further oxidation.

The amount of energy derived from the different basic foodstuffs varies. On oxidation, one gram of carbohydrate yields 4.2 kcal; * one gram of protein, 4.3 kcal; and one gram of fat, 9.5 kcal. Thus, the energy value of fat is about twice that of the other major foodstuffs. A man in a sedentary occupation needs some 2500 kcal per day; a workman needs 4000–5000 or more. If a man remains completely at rest, he needs about 1500 kcal just to keep the body processes going.

The energy expended by an animal is supplied by its food intake, and if the food intake is insufficient, the remaining caloric requirement is covered by the consumption of body substances, primarily fat. If the food intake is greater than the energy used, the surplus is deposited as fat, whatever the nature of the food is. For example, a pig can be fattened up on a diet containing a surplus of starch (grain or corn). Since fat yields twice as many calories per gram as carbohydrates, it is better suited for storing energy in animals. In sessile animals, such as oysters and mussels, where weight is of minor consequence, carbohydrate (glycogen) is used for storage. Intestinal parasites, such as *Ascaris,* also store glycogen. Glycogen is possibly a more suitable storage substance in these animals because they frequently live under conditions of low oxygen supply—the intestine has a low oxygen concentration because of bacterial fermentation, and mussels frequently close their shells for long periods, letting in little water. Since glycogen, by breaking down to lactic acid, can yield a considerable amount of energy in the absence of oxygen, it may be advantageous for these animals to store glycogen rather than fat.

BUILDING AND MAINTENANCE. Although proteins can be used for energy, they are more important as structural substances. Aside from water, the main constituent of most cells is protein. Each protein molecule consists of from about 100 to several thousand amino acid molecules bound together by peptide bonds.† However, no more than about 20 different amino acids commonly occur in proteins. They are joined together in characteristic fashion so that each animal or plant species has different, specific proteins, and even individuals within a species may have characteristically different proteins. For example, the blood groups in man depend on different structures of some of the blood proteins.

In the process of digestion, food protein is split into single amino acids which are absorbed from the intestine. The amino acids are subsequently synthesized to species-specific proteins in the body. The amino acids can either be supplied in the diet or be formed in the body from other amino

* One calorie (cal) is the amount of heat necessary to heat one gram of water from 14.5°C to 15.5°C. One kilocalorie (kcal) is 1000 calories.

† See the volume in this series, W. D. McElroy, *Cell Physiology and Biochemistry,* 2nd ed. (Englewood Cliffs, N. J.: Prentice-Hall, 1964).

acids. Those amino acids that cannot be so formed and must be supplied in the diet are called *essential amino acids*. In man, eight of the 20 or so common amino acids are essential. On page 8 we saw how the cow utilizes microbial protein synthesis; since the microbes can form all amino acids, the cow apparently does not need any essential amino acids.

Plants do synthesize protein from inorganic nitrogen (ammonia or nitrate), and some microbes can even use atmospheric nitrogen (the process is called *nitrogen fixation*). The amino acids in animal protein, therefore, are ultimately of plant or microbial origin.

ACCESSORY FOODSTUFFS, VITAMINS.   In addition to the major foodstuffs, animals need a number of other substances in smaller amounts. For historical reasons, these *accessory foodstuffs* are called *vitamins*. When it was first discovered that certain human diseases (nonmicrobial ones) could be caused by the absence of dietary components, it was believed that these components, chemically, were amines. Later, this notion was proven wrong, but the name applied then, *vitamin,* has remained in the language. In the early part of the twentieth century, various unidentified factors were named vitamin A, vitamin B, etc., but as the chemical constitution has been clarified, we now often prefer to use the chemical names.

The metabolic role of some vitamins is well known, but others are not as well understood. Thus, man needs ascorbic acid (vitamin C), but its exact metabolic function is unknown. Vitamin A is attached to a protein in the vertebrate eye and is necessary for normal sensitivity to light; its chemistry is known (the name vitamin A is preferred for simplicity), but the mechanism that transforms the chemical effect of light on the retina to an impulse in the optic nerve is not understood. We now know the role of thiamin (vitamin B_1), which has been accurately pinpointed as a constituent of an important enzyme system that is required for sugar metabolism and that participates in all the oxidative decarboxylation that leads to the formation of CO_2.

Vitamins are needed only in minute quantities, a few milligrams or a fraction of a milligram per day, but not all animals have the same vitamin requirements. If a substance is necessary and must be supplied in the food, it obviously cannot be synthesized in the body, and thus the need for a vitamin indicates a synthetic disability of the organism. Ascorbic acid (vitamin C), which prevents scurvy, is a dietary requirement for man, monkeys, and the guinea pig, but all other mammals seem able to synthesize it. Vitamin K, which is necessary for blood coagulation, is synthesized in mammals by intestinal bacteria. Its role was first discovered in birds, who require it in their food, and only later was its role in mammals established. Deficiency of vitamin K occurs in man when intestinal absorption is inadequate—for example, when obstruction of the bile duct causes the absence of bile salts, or when the bacterial flora of the intestine is changed during prolonged use of certain antibiotics.

MINERALS AND TRACE ELEMENTS. The blood and tissues of animals contain various salts, some in solution, others not. *Sodium* and *potassium* are the predominant cations, *chloride* and *bicarbonate* the principal anions. Other ions present are *calcium, magnesium, phosphate,* and *sulfate.* The total salt concentration in mammalian blood is about 0.9 per cent.

Calcium phosphate (hydroxyapatite) is the major constituent of vertebrate bones and teeth, while invertebrate shells are mainly calcium carbonate. In some radiolaria (protozoa), the shell contains strontium, an element that is present in sea water in minute amounts.

Iron is a necessary constituent of the hemoglobin of blood, but the total amount present is not very great, about 4.3 grams in an adult man. Unless there is a blood loss, the dietary need for iron is very small, although, of course, children need it during growth and adult women require it to replace the menstrual loss.

A number of other elements are found in even smaller quantities. Some of them have known metabolic roles—for example, *iodine* is found in the hormone produced by the thyroid gland, *copper* is essential for the synthesis of hemoglobin (although it is not a part of the hemoglobin molecule), *cobalt* is part of vitamin B_{12} (essential for blood formation), and *zinc* is necessary for the activity of some enzymes. The amounts needed are very small; for some of the elements a deficiency almost never occurs, for others, such as iodine, a nutritional deficiency is common where the content of the element in the soil is particularly low. This lack can, of course, be corrected by the addition of a trace of iodine to the diet, as is customarily done by adding a minute amount to table salt. A deficiency of cobalt has been an important deterrent to the production of sheep in parts of Australia. The afflicted animals have anemia, their appetite is impaired, they lose weight, and die from inanition. Once the disease is understood as a cobalt deficiency, the situation can be remedied with small doses of that element.

Other elements, including *aluminum, silicon, lead, nickel*—in fact, almost all the elements from the periodic table—can be found in some minute amount, and it is possible that some of them may have an unknown and essential role while others are present only incidentally.

Oxygen

CHAPTER TWO

Since energy for animals is provided by the oxidation of foodstuffs, oxygen is as important as food in maintaining life. The uptake of oxygen and simultaneous release of carbon dioxide is called *respiration*. In very small animals, sufficient oxygen can be taken up through the general body surface, but in most animals special *respiratory organs* are necessary for gas exchange.

In many larger animals, the *blood* must bring the oxygen from the respiratory organs to the various parts of the body. The blood, however, has other functions as well, and in some animals (insects, for example) its role in gas transport is insignificant. The blood is pumped throughout the organism by the heart; since the blood returns to the heart to be re-circulated, the system of blood vessels and heart is called the *circulatory system.*

A few animals can live when oxygen is absent (anaerobic conditions)—for example, intestinal parasites have almost no oxygen available to them. By a process we call *anaerobic metabolism,* they are able to utilize the energy from chemical processes, such as the formation of lactic acid from glucose,* that do not require oxygen. Anaerobic metabolism is not as unique as it sounds—for instance, lactic acid is regularly formed in muscles that work heavily.

RESPIRATION

Gases in Air and Water

The atmosphere contains about one-fifth oxygen, four-fifths nitrogen, a minute amount of carbon dioxide, and a variable amount of water vapor. Molecular nitrogen is completely inert to the animal organism and plays no greater role than the true inert gases (helium, neon, argon, etc.) that are present in a small amount (about 1 per cent). In physiology, it is therefore customary to lump these gases and simply call them nitrogen. The proportion of gases in atmospheric air is extremely constant, and remains the same from sea level to the highest mountain tops (Table 2-1).

Table 2-1

THE COMPOSITION OF DRY ATMOSPHERIC AIR

Gas	*Per cent*
Oxygen (O_2)	20.95
Carbon dioxide (CO_2)	0.03
Nitrogen (N_2)	79.02

The atmospheric gases are soluble in water. The amount dissolved depends on (a) the concentration of the gas in the air, (b) the solubility of the particular gas in question, and (c) the temperature. The amount of oxygen dissolved is of particular importance to aquatic animals; from ordinary air with 21 per cent oxygen, about 1 ml of oxygen is dissolved in 100 ml of water at 0°C. With increasing temperature, the solubility for gases decreases; at 15°, for example, the solubility is 0.7 ml O_2/100 ml and at 37° about 0.5 ml O_2/100 ml.

With an increase in atmospheric pressure, more gas is dissolved in the water. Since the normal atmospheric pressure is 760 mm Hg,† and 21 per cent of this is oxygen, the *partial pressure* of oxygen is 159 mm Hg. The amounts of dissolved oxygen listed in the preceding paragraph are the

---

* The complete oxidation of one mole of glucose yields 686 kcal. The splitting of glucose into lactic acid ($C_6H_{12}O_6 \longrightarrow 2C_3H_6O_3$) yields 56 kcal per mole glucose, or about 8 per cent of the total available energy.

† The pressure of gases is expressed in mm of mercury (Hg), which indicates the height of the mercury column that can be supported by the particular gas pressure. Hence, atmospheric pressure corresponds to the height of the mercury column in a mercury barometer.

amounts found in water when it is in equilibrium with a normal atmosphere whose partial pressure of oxygen is 159 mm Hg. We then say that 159 mm is the *tension* of oxygen in the water. Thus, the tension for a gas in solution equals the partial pressure of the gas in the atmosphere in equilibrium with the solution. If the partial pressure of oxygen in the air is reduced, less is dissolved in the water, and since the atmospheric pressure decreases with altitude, the amount of oxygen that is dissolved also decreases. At 18,000 feet, the atmospheric pressure is one-half that at sea level, and the amount of dissolved oxygen is also one-half.

Carbon dioxide (CO_2) is about 30 times as soluble as oxygen. When it is dissolved in water it forms carbonic acid (H_2CO_3), which, like other acids, forms salts (carbonates and bicarbonates). When cations such as sodium or calcium are present, much of the carbon dioxide that enters into solution will be found in bicarbonates or carbonates. This is frequently the case in natural water, and in the body fluids and blood, sodium bicarbonate is one of the most important buffer substances.

Nitrogen, which is somewhat less soluble in water than oxygen, plays no biological role, except under very special circumstances. If a man is exposed to a sudden reduction in pressure, such as an aviator experiences when he ascends rapidly in a nonpressurized cabin, his blood may become filled with nitrogen bubbles in the same way that bubbles are formed in a soda-water bottle when the cap is taken off and the pressure suddenly reduced. These bubbles block the fine blood vessels and cause decompression sickness, or the bends, which is a serious hazard also in divers that ascend from depths of some 30 to 40 feet or more.

Respiratory Organs

In very small animals (e.g., protozoans), gas exchange is not a complex problem, for enough oxygen can penetrate from the surface to all parts of the organism. This may also be the case in animals that are somewhat larger, such as earthworms, but if an animal has a relatively high rate of oxygen consumption and is more than a few millimeters in its smallest dimension, sufficient oxygen cannot be supplied by diffusion through the general body surface. Such animals therefore have special respiratory organs, which always have a greatly enlarged surface through which oxygen can diffuse. There are three types of respiratory organs: (a) gills, (b) lungs, and (c) tracheae.

If the respiratory surface of an animal is turned in to form a cavity, we call it a *lung,* but if it is enlarged by being turned out, we call the appendage a *gill.* Usually gills are connected with water-breathing, and are unsuited for respiration in air. If a fish is removed from water, the soft gill filaments stick together and the greater part of the gill surface will not be reached by air. In some cases, gills may be modified for air-breathing and are then usually covered or located in cavities (in sowbugs and woodlice) that help reduce the evaporation of water. Since the thin surfaces of the gills of aquatic animals are easily damaged, they, too, are often protected in a gill cavity (fish, crabs).

The insects have a peculiar type of respiratory organ which pipes oxygen directly to the tissues. Fine tubes lead from openings *(spiracles)* on the insect's surface to every part of the body. These tubes, or *tracheae,* branch repeatedly, and the finest branches, which are less than a thousandth of a millimeter in diameter, penetrate everywhere in the body. Thus, the characteristic of a tracheal system is that it carries oxygen directly to the tissues, whereas in gills and lungs, the oxygen is taken up by the blood, which carries it to other parts of the body.

In water-breathing animals, oxygen is constantly removed from the water in contact with the gill, so the water needs to be replaced. Similarly, the air in a lung or tracheal system must be renewed. Since oxygen in the atmosphere is present in a high and constant concentration, respiration in air is in some respects far superior to respiration in water. A fifth of the air is oxygen, and the amount of inert gas that is moved in and out of the lungs is only some four times the weight of the oxygen. An aquatic animal is in a much less favorable position. Even when the water is saturated with oxygen, it contains only 0.7 ml oxygen (about one mg) per 100 ml water (at 15°C). The oxygen is therefore contained in 100,000 times its weight of water.

Obviously, in order to ventilate a respiratory system with water, a tremendous bulk of water must be moved, which of course requires energy; in air, in contrast, nitrogen that weighs only four times as much as the oxygen has to be moved. One further advantage of respiration in air is that the rate of diffusion of oxygen is 300,000 times as rapid as it is in water. It is not surprising, then, that the warm-blooded animals, with their high metabolic rate and need for oxygen, have evolved as air breathers, and that this group also includes the largest animals in existence. The greatest disadvantage of air breathing and terrestrial life in general is the danger of desiccation, which we shall discuss in a later chapter.

Respiration in Mammals

To function properly, the lung must renew the air it contains at a rate that is adjusted to the rate at which oxygen is used and carbon dioxide is produced. The process of air renewal we shall discuss under the *mechanics of respiration,* the proper rate adjustment under *regulation of respiration;* under *gas exchange in the lungs* we shall describe how gases enter and leave the blood.

MECHANICS OF RESPIRATION.   The lungs occupy most of the chest cavity, which is bounded on the sides by the ribs and toward the abdomen by the diaphragm. In inspiration, muscles pull the ribs up and out, and the muscular diaphragm contracts and flattens so that the entire chest expands. The lungs are thus enlarged and air is pulled in through the trachea. The amount of air that moves in or out with a single breath is called the *tidal volume*. In a man at rest, the tidal volume is about 500 ml but, as we all know, the lungs have a far greater capacity than just breathing at rest. The total capacity for breathing (that is, the amount of air that can be exhaled after the lungs have been filled to capacity) is called the *vital capacity* and is about 4000 ml (4 liters), although it varies a great deal from individual to individual. Men usually have a higher vital capacity than women, and training can increase the capacity appreciably. Athletes have a much higher vital capacity than the average person, often 5 to 6 liters or more.

Even when we try to exhale as much as possible, some air, called the *residual volume* (about 1.5 liters), still remains in our lungs. Therefore, we can never fill our lungs completely with fresh air, for all air that is inhaled is mixed with air already present in the lungs. The amount of fresh air taken into the lungs is about 10 liters per minute in rest. In exercise, the ventilation of the lungs increases and may, in heavy exercise, reach 125 liters per minute.

REGULATION OF RESPIRATION. The renewal of air in the lungs is accurately adjusted to the need for oxygen, and the regulation of the breathing movements is very precise. The muscles of the chest and the diaphragm are controlled by nerves that originate in the spinal cord. The *respiratory center,* in the medulla oblongata, is the place where information about the need for ventilation is received and coordinated. The most important single factor in the regulation of respiration is the sensitivity of the respiratory center to the carbon dioxide tension of the blood. If this tension increases only slightly, breathing immediately becomes deeper and faster, permitting more carbon dioxide to leave the blood, until the carbon dioxide level has returned to normal. This regulation of the tension of carbon dioxide is so exact that its concentration in the lung always remains virtually constant.

The respiratory center is quite insensitive to the oxygen concentration in the blood, although if there is a serious decrease in oxygen concentration, sensitive organs (chemoreceptors) in the aorta and the carotid arteries send impulses to the respiratory center that generate an increase in respiration. We can easily show that carbon dioxide is more important than oxygen in regulating respiration. If the amount of carbon dioxide in the inhaled air is raised to a few per cent, the ventilation of the lungs is more than doubled (Fig. 2-1), but a decrease in oxygen by a few per cent has no effect whatsoever. It is a curious fact that regulation of respiration depends primarily on accumulation of carbon dioxide and not on lack of oxygen. This is not true in all animals, however. Among higher animals, those that are good divers, such as seals, are peculiarly insensitive to carbon dioxide. Among lower animals, those that are aquatic do not depend on CO_2 for regulation of respiration, primarily because CO_2 is so easily soluble in water that it does not accumulate to any great extent.

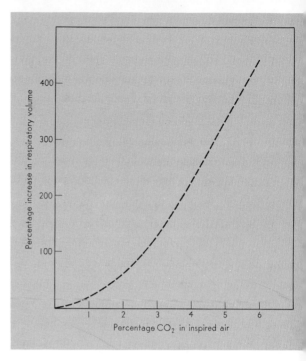

Fig. 2-1. If the carbon dioxide concentration in the inspired air is increased, the volume of respiration increases to many times the normal level. This increase, of course, does not lead to a corresponding increase in oxygen uptake. (From R. W. Scott, American Journal of Physiology, 44, 1917.)

Since respiration is under automatic control, we usually pay no attention to it. If we wish, however, we can hold our breath for a short time, perhaps a minute or two. When we do so, carbon dioxide accumulates in the blood, and the effect on the respiratory center increases until the stimulus is so strong that it overrides the voluntary inhibition. For this reason, it is impossible for you to asphyxiate yourself by simply holding your breath.

When you take a series of deep breaths before swimming under water, you can stay under longer. The increased ventilation of the lungs does not increase the oxygen content of the arterial blood. It does, however, remove more than the usual amount of carbon dioxide from the blood, and it takes longer, then, to build up carbon dioxide to the point where the respiratory center cannot be held in abeyance. (Voluntary over-ventilation of the lungs can be carried so far that the loss of CO_2 from the blood causes loss of consciousness, owing to the decrease in carbonic acid and the ensuing shift of the pH in an alkaline direction.)

GAS EXCHANGE IN THE LUNGS. The blood coming to the lungs from the heart has a low oxygen content and a high CO_2 content. In the lungs oxygen enters the blood, and CO_2 leaves it. Figure 2-2 indicates that the partial pressure of oxygen in the lung (which always is lower than in the atmosphere) is higher than in the venous blood. Therefore, oxygen diffuses into the blood until the tension has reached that of the alveolar air. The membrane that separates the air from the blood is very thin, about 0.001–0.002 mm, and gases penetrate it readily. Since the oxygen moves by diffusion, its tension in the blood never exceeds that in the alveolar air.

Carbon dioxide leaves the blood by diffusion, as is illustrated in Fig. 2-2. It is important to note that far from all the CO_2 is removed from the blood in the lung and, similarly, that venous blood still contains much oxygen when it returns to the lungs.

In a man at rest, the blood takes up about 200–250 ml of oxygen per minute as it passes through the lungs. In work, this amount is greater and may increase as much as fifteen times, to around 3000 ml per minute. This much oxygen can diffuse into the blood partly because the membrane is so thin and partly because its surface is so large. In the lungs of man, the blood comes in contact with a total surface of about 100 m^2 (or 1000 square feet).

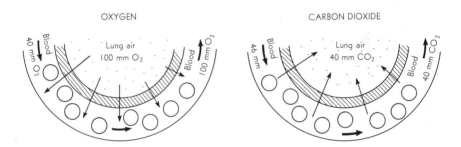

Fig. 2-2. When blood that is low in oxygen reaches the lungs, oxygen enters the blood until its tension equals that of the alveolar air. Similarly, the blood gives off CO_2 in the lung until its tension equals that in the lung, which, as we have seen, remains quite constant. Arterial blood, therefore, has a very constant content of oxygen as well as of CO_2.

A Special Problem—The Swimbladder of Fish

Many aquatic animals have devices that lower the specific gravity of their bodies and thus help them to float in water. In particular, planktonic organisms often contain fat droplets that bring their specific gravity down to that of water, so that they remain floating without sinking to the bottom. Some organisms have a more elaborate system, consisting of air or gas floats (Fig. 2-3). Gas floats are found in a few species of protozoans, coelenterates, molluscs, and insects. In fishes, on the other hand, gas floats called *swimbladders* are quite common, and about one-half of all bony fishes have them.

Since the specific gravity of the fish body is higher than that of water, a fish without a swimbladder would have to swim constantly to keep from sinking in the water. If the fish can acquire a volume of air in its body, however, it can reduce its specific gravity to that of water and will not have to work to stay at a particular level in the water. Unlike pelagic fishes,

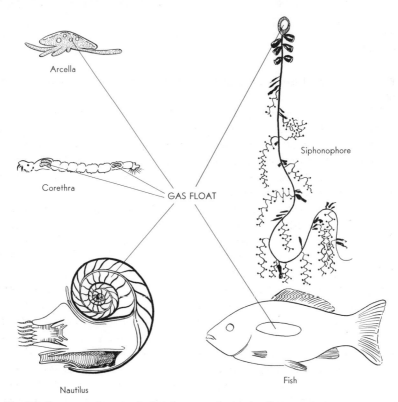

Fig. 2-3. Some aquatic animals that have gas floats. Arcella, a protozoan, reacts to a low oxygen content in the water by forming gas bubbles which carry it to the surface where oxygen is available. The other animals are a mosquito larva (Corethra or Chaoborus), a mollusc (Nautilus), a coelenterate (siphonophore), and a fish—all use their gas floats to maintain buoyancy in the water. (Original drawing by Dr. R. Fänge, University of Gothenburg, Sweden.)

which almost always have a swimbladder, fishes living at the bottom do not need, and seldom have, swimbladders. The volume of the swimbladder is usually about 4 to 7 per cent of the body volume, just sufficient to make the fish buoyant. Since sea water has a higher specific gravity than fresh water, less air is needed to keep a salt-water fish floating, and the swimbladder is usually somewhat smaller in marine than in fresh-water fishes.

A fish with a certain amount of gas in the swimbladder is in equilibrium only at one particular level. If it rises in the water, the swimbladder increases in volume because of the reduced pressure, and, to regain buoyancy, the fish must give off gases. In some fishes, the swimbladder is connected to the esophagus via a duct and air can be let out through this passageway, but many fish have no such duct and give off the gases to the blood in a special gas-resorbing part of the bladder. In the opposite situation, when a fish descends to a lower level, the bladder is compressed and the fish becomes heavier than the water. Buoyancy can then be regained only if the fish adds more gas to the bladder to increase its volume, and this is done by means of a special structure located in the swimbladder, the *gas gland,* which removes dissolved gas from the blood and secretes it into the swim-bladder.

The easiest way to study the composition of the secreted gas is to with-draw some of it from the swimbladder into a syringe fitted with a needle. To regain buoyancy, the fish now secretes gas into the swimbladder, and the composition of this gas is representative of what the gland ordinarily secretes. Most fishes have been found to secrete a gas that is high in oxygen, and since the tension in the arterial blood is only one-fifth of an atmosphere, the fish must actively secrete the gas against the much higher pressure inside the swimbladder. In fishes that live at great depth, the pressure inside the swimbladder is very high—for example, at 500 meters (about 1500 feet) it is 50 atmospheres. At this depth, the tension of oxygen dissolved in the water is the same as at the surface, one-fifth of an atmos-phere, and the swimbladder gas, which is mostly oxygen, must be secreted into a pressure that is several hundred times its tension in the water.

Some fishes—in particular, whitefish—have very high concentrations of nitrogen in the swimbladder. This is difficult to explain, for there is no known way of binding molecular nitrogen in the animal organism. Al-though we do not understand the process, we strongly suspect that it in-volves physical rather than chemical principles, for argon is also present in an amount similar to that in the atmosphere (about 1 per cent of the quantity of nitrogen). Since argon is an inert gas that cannot undergo chemical combination, it must have entered by "physical" processes.

Our knowledge of the secretion of gases into the floats of invertebrate animals is woefully lacking, and is a field where investigation is likely to yield extremely interesting results. It has recently been found, for example, that one of the gases in the float of the Portuguese Man-of-War *(Physalia)* is carbon monoxide, which, as we know, is highly poisonous to higher animals.

BLOOD

Functions of Blood

In very small animals, oxygen penetrates the surface and diffuses to all parts of the organism, but in larger animals a special transport system, the blood, becomes necessary. Gas transport, however, is not the only function of blood. In the more highly organized animals, the blood has a number of functions, and the most important are:

1. Transport of *oxygen* from the site of uptake to all parts of the body; and the transportation in the opposite direction of *carbon dioxide* produced by the cells.

2. Transportation of *nutrients* from the gastrointestinal tract to the various parts of the body where they are used or stored.

3. Transportation of *excretory products* from cells or organs where they are formed to the organs of excretion (kidney).

4. Transportation of *metabolic products* that are formed in one part of the body to other parts where they are used; also the transportation of nutrients from storage to places where they are needed.

5. The blood also serves as a *communication system* within the body by transporting substances that regulate the function of certain organs. An example is the hormone *secretin,* which controls the secretion from the pancreas (see p. 6).

6. The blood functions in certain kinds of *movement*. For example, when a newly hatched butterfly emerges from the pupa, it expands its wings by pumping blood into them and keeps them expanded until they harden in the air.

Blood also has the ability to *coagulate* and thus prevent undue blood loss if blood vessels are damaged.

GAS TRANSPORT.   Most of the transportation problems listed above can be taken care of by any aqueous medium, but an adequate transport of gases needs special adaptations. The solubility of oxygen in water is rather low, but this shortcoming is overcome by the fact that the oxygen is bound to carrier substances in the blood. In mammalian blood, the oxygen carrier is *hemoglobin*, a protein which is found in the red blood cells; the blood fluid, or *plasma,* contains no hemoglobin. The presence of the hemoglobin is very important, for the plasma alone contains only about 0.3 ml dissolved oxygen per 100 ml. The presence of the red cells increases the amount to about 20 ml oxygen per 100 ml blood; thus, the hemoglobin is responsible for almost all the oxygen carried in the blood.

Hemoglobin is found in all vertebrates, and also in some invertebrates (certain mollusks, arthropods, and annelids). In the invertebrates, the hemoglobin is not enclosed in corpuscles but is dissolved in the blood fluid. This difference is important, for the location of the hemoglobin inside cells permits the blood to carry far greater amounts of it. If all the hemoglobin from the red cells of man were free in the blood, the average protein concentration in the blood would be about 20 per cent. Since such a concentrated protein solution flows about as heavily as syrup, the heart would have to do a tremendous amount of work to pump the blood through the blood vessels. Animals that have the hemoglobin dissolved in the blood fluid, therefore, have much stricter limitations on how much hemoglobin the blood contains.

Only relatively few invertebrates have hemoglobin, and many, particularly mollusks and arthropods, have another oxygen carrier, *hemocyanin*. Hemoglobin always contains iron; hemocyanin contains copper. It is blue in color when combined with oxygen, and colorless when the oxygen is given up; it is always present in solution and never in blood cells. Although hemoglobin and hemocyanin are the two commonest oxygen carriers, there

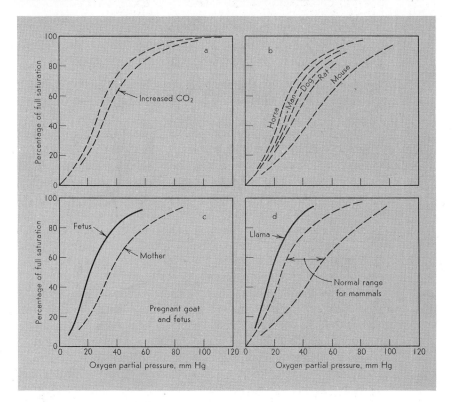

Fig. 2-4. The oxygen dissociation curve shows how the amount of oxyhemoglobin (ordinate) is related to oxygen pressure (abscissa). A curve located to the right signifies that oxygen is more readily given up by the hemoglobin. Increased carbon dioxide shifts the curve to the right (a). Small animals that need more oxygen per gram tissue have blood that more readily gives up oxygen (b). The fetus has blood that binds oxygen more readily than does that of the mother (c). The llama, which lives at the low oxygen pressure of the high Andes, has blood which binds oxygen more readily than does that of other mammals (d).

are others as well. All share one characteristic: Each contains a metal combined with a protein in such a way that oxygen can be bound reversibly.

OXYGEN DISSOCIATION CURVE. At high oxygen pressure, the hemoglobin combines with oxygen to form oxyhemoglobin. Each iron atom can bind one oxygen molecule, and when all sites are occupied, the hemoglobin cannot take on any more; it is fully loaded or *saturated*. At low oxygen pressure, oxygen dissociates from its binding, and the hemoglobin will eventually give up all its oxygen. At any given oxygen concentration, there is a definite proportion between the amount of hemoglobin and oxyhemoglobin. How this proportion is related to the oxygen concentration can best be expressed in the *oxygen dissociation curve* (Fig. 2-4). This curve shows that the hemoglobin is completely saturated with oxygen at the oxygen partial pressure of the alveolar air, about 100–110 mm Hg. At higher oxygen pressure, no more oxygen is bound by the hemoglobin. At lower oxygen pressure, oxygen is given off, and at 30 mm oxygen pressure, half the hemo-

23

globin is present as oxyhemoglobin. As the oxygen pressure decreases further, more oxygen is given off, and all is given up when the oxygen pressure reaches zero.

The oxygen dissociation curve is influenced by carbon dioxide. An increase in carbon dioxide shifts the curve to the right (Fig. 2-4a), a displacement that is called the *Bohr effect* after one of its discoverers, Christian Bohr.* A higher CO_2 concentration therefore causes more oxygen to be given up at any given oxygen pressure, a result that is of significance in the tissues, for as the blood in a capillary gives off oxygen, carbon dioxide enters from the tissues and increases the amount of oxygen that is given off from the hemoglobin. Thus, the Bohr effect facilitates the delivery of additional oxygen to the tissues.

The dissociation curve is not the same for all animals (Fig. 2-4b). In general, small animals have a dissociation curve located to the right, a displacement that is probably related to the much higher metabolic rate of the tissues in small animals. When the curve is to the right, it means that oxygen is given off more readily; when located to the left, it indicates that the binding of oxygen to the hemoglobin is firmer. The small animal needs to have oxygen supplied to the tissues at a higher rate, and this demand is better satisfied by the higher unloading pressure.

For a number of animals, including man, the dissociation curve of the fetus is located to the left of that of the mother (Fig. 2-4c). This is important for the fetus, since its blood must take up all its oxygen from the maternal blood in the placenta. With the fetal blood having greater affinity for oxygen, the oxygen will tend to leave the maternal and enter the fetal blood, and thus, at a given oxygen pressure, the fetal blood becomes more saturated than the maternal blood. After birth, the fetal type of hemoglobin gradually disappears and is replaced by the adult type. Similar displacements to the left of the dissociation curve have been found in the developing chick and in the frog tadpole. These live where oxygen is less readily available than in the atmosphere, and it is an advantage for them that the hemoglobin becomes saturated at a relatively low oxygen pressure.

A displacement to the left is also found in the llama, which lives in the high Andes of South America (Fig. 2-4d), and this better enables its blood to take up oxygen at the low pressures of high altitude. This characteristic is also found in llamas that have lived all their lives in zoos at sea level; in other words, the adaptation to high altitude is an inherited character.

CARBON MONOXIDE POISONING.   Carbon monoxide is well known as the toxic component in coal gas and the exhaust fumes from automobiles. It has caused many accidental deaths and has been employed in suicides. It combines very readily with hemoglobin, thereby preventing the hemoglobin from taking up oxygen, and death results from asphyxiation produced by the blocking of oxygen transport.

* The father of the eminent Danish physicist Niels Bohr.

Since hemoglobin's affinity for carbon monoxide is about 300 times as high as its affinity for oxygen, a very small amount of carbon monoxide in the air will bind most of the hemoglobin. As little as 0.1 per cent of carbon monoxide in the air is dangerous and will cause serious symptoms in about 30 to 60 minutes.

CARBON DIOXIDE TRANSPORT. The total amount of carbon dioxide in venous blood is about 60 ml per 100 ml blood. In the lungs, about 10 ml of CO_2 are given off, and the arterial blood contains about 50 ml total CO_2 per 100 ml. Thus, a relatively small fraction of the carbon dioxide present is given off in the lungs. Only part of the carbon dioxide in blood is in simple solution; most of it is present in the form of sodium bicarbonate. As CO_2 enters the blood from the tissues, it combines with water to form carbonic acid (H_2CO_3), which dissociates to hydrogen ions (H^+) and bicarbonate ions (HCO_3^-). The latter, with sodium ions in the plasma, make up sodium bicarbonate. Together with carbonic acid, sodium bicarbonate forms a buffer system that tends to maintain a relatively constant pH of the blood.

Coagulation of Blood

When a blood sample is drawn, it remains liquid for a few minutes only, and then turns into a gel. This process is called *clotting* or *coagulation*. Although blood has the ability to clot, it normally does not clot in the blood vessels. If a blood sample is examined on a glass slide under the microscope, we can see fine thread-like structures forming a network. This network, which produces the clot, consists of the protein *fibrin* (the name is derived from the fibrous structure of the clot), and it in turn is formed from another protein, *fibrinogen,* which makes up about 0.3 per cent of the blood. The conversion of fibrinogen to fibrin is catalyzed by an enzyme, *thrombin,* and the reason the blood does not clot in the blood vessels is that this enzyme is absent from the circulating blood. How, then, does coagulation start when the blood is outside the vascular system?

Fig. 2-5. The main events of blood clotting. The clot formation is due to a catalyzed change of the soluble protein fibrinogen to the insoluble fibrin. The formation of the catalyzing enzyme (thrombin) is explained in the text.

It has been found that a precursor of thrombin called *prothrombin* is present in the plasma (Fig. 2-5) and is activated by another enzyme, *thromboplastin,* which is released from damaged tissues and from a special type of blood cell known as the blood platelets. The action of thromboplastin requires the presence of *calcium* ions, which are normally present in blood plasma. The one factor necessary to start the clot-

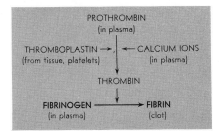

PROTHROMBIN
(in plasma)

THROMBOPLASTIN → ↓ ← CALCIUM IONS
(from tissue, platelets) (in plasma)

THROMBIN

FIBRINOGEN ⟶ FIBRIN
(in plasma) (clot)

ting of blood, therefore, is thromboplastin. The blood platelets (there are about one-half million per cubic millimeter of blood) are extremely sensitive to contact with damaged tissue or with such foreign substances as glass. They disintegrate and release thromboplastin; the prothrombin is immediately converted to thrombin, which catalyses the transformation of the soluble fibrinogen to the insoluble fibrin.

PREVENTION OF COAGULATION—ANTICOAGULANTS. Since calcium ions are necessary for the action of thromboplastin, coagulation of the blood can be prevented by removing the calcium. This can be done by adding compounds that bind calcium, such as sodium oxalate or sodium citrate; by such additions, blood can be kept liquid in a test tube for an unlimited time, although the addition of calcium will bring about immediate coagulation.

Besides the removal of calcium, clotting can be prevented in several other ways. One clotting inhibitor, *heparin,* can be isolated from liver. It is widely used in medicine, and acts by interfering with the conversion of prothrombin to thrombin. Prothrombin is formed in the liver, and vitamin K is necessary for this synthesis. In its absence prothrombin is not formed, and the blood will not coagulate. Vitamin K is normally formed by bacteria in the intestine of mammals, and so a deficiency occurs only when its absorption is insufficient (see p. 11).

The synthesis by the liver of prothrombin can be inhibited by a number of substances. One is dicoumarol, which is formed in clover hay when it becomes spoiled. Such hay is highly toxic to livestock, for it causes internal bleedings, an effect that is also utilized in many rat poisons. Usually, rats have an uncanny ability to avoid poisoned baits, but if they can be lured into eating certain substances similar to dicoumarol, they will die from internal bleedings without becoming aware of having eaten poison. Other anticoagulants that inhibit the action of thrombin are those found in the saliva of blood-sucking animals (such as leeches and mosquitoes). This anticoagulant action is necessary to prevent clotting of the blood in the fine mouth-parts of those animals. Certain snake venoms, in contrast, contain substances that cause a very rapid coagulation of blood, and this effect contributes to the speed with which the victim succumbs.

CIRCULATION

If blood is to fulfill its function as a transport medium, it must move quickly and efficiently. In vertebrates, the blood is carried in a system of elastic pipes, the *blood vessels,* through which it is pumped by the *heart.* Since the blood returns to the heart without leaving the blood vessels, it remains in a closed system which we call a "closed circulation." In many invertebrates—crabs, for example—the blood pumped out by the heart soon leaves the blood vessels and flows more or less freely between tissues and organs. This system is called an "open circulation" and is, in many ways, less efficient than a closed system. The main advantages of a closed system of blood vessels are these: (a) The blood is piped directly to the organs where it is needed; (b) the amount flowing to a certain organ can be regulated by changing the diameter of the blood vessels; and (c) the blood returns rapidly to the heart.

The structure of the circulatory system in mammals and birds is shown in Fig. 2-6. Although the circulatory system is simpler in lower vertebrates, the main features are the same: The *heart* pumps the blood through the *arteries* out into the finest branches of blood vessels, the *capillaries,* and then back through the *veins* to the heart.

THE HEART.   The wall of the heart is a muscle that contracts with considerable force, squeezing the blood out into the arteries. Each half of the heart is a two-chambered pump, consisting of the relatively thin-walled *auricle,* and the thick-walled *ventricle,* which contracts with great force. The contraction of the heart is called *systole,* the relaxation *diastole.* When

Fig. 2-6. The circulation of blood in mammals can be followed in this diagram. The blood arriving from the tissues enters the right auricle and is pumped through the pulmonary arteries to the lungs, where carbon dioxide is given off and oxygen taken up. The blood returns via the pulmonary veins to the left side of the heart, which pumps it through the aorta to the various parts of the body. The tissues use oxygen, and carbon dioxide is added to the blood, which then returns in the veins to the right side of the heart. The right and left parts of the heart have a common muscular wall, but this diagram shows them slightly separated to emphasize that each acts as a separate pump.

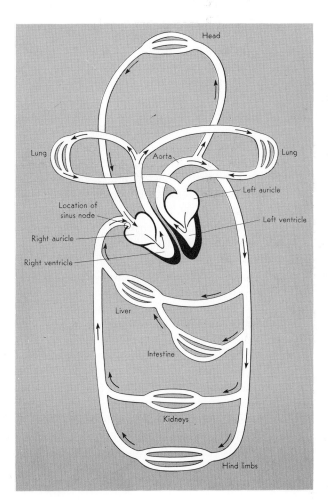

the contraction starts in the auricle, the blood is forced into the ventricle, the contraction spreads to the ventricle, and valves prevent a backflow into the now relaxed auricle, forcing the blood into the arteries. Since the wall of the ventricle is thick and not easily distended, the pressure from the veins alone is insufficient to fill the ventricle, and the auricle helps by acting as a priming pump. Thus, the two chambers work in series to build up the high pressure needed in the circulation of higher animals. The right and left halves of the heart beat synchronously, logically enough, for as a certain volume of blood is pumped out of the left side of the heart, an equal volume must enter the right side. The output of the two halves must be the same, but the right ventricle has a thinner wall because less pressure is necessary to force the blood through the capillaries of the lung than through the rest of the body.

The heart muscle receives its nutrition and oxygen supply through the *coronary artery,* which branches off from the aorta a short distance from the left ventricle. Pumping continuously, day and night, for a lifetime at a rate of 70 or more contractions per minute (or 100,000 in 24 hours), this muscle performs a prodigious amount of sustained work. The only rest it gets is in the short fraction of a second between contractions. Each stroke of the heart pumps out about 60 ml of blood (from each side), and, at a pulse rate of 70, the output of the heart is about four liters per minute. In heavy work, the stroke volume increases to around 200 ml, and the rate increases about threefold to over 200 strokes per minute, resulting in a cardiac output of 40 liters per minute, or ten times the resting value.

The heart muscle consists of a meshwork, or *syncytium,* of interconnected muscle fibers, and it is through this connected structure that a contraction spreads, starting in the auricles at the *sinus node,* which is near the place where the veins enter the auricle, sweeping across the entire auricle, and then to the ventricle. The heart muscle can contract without stimulation from nerves, for in the embryo the developing heart begins to pulsate before any nerves have grown into it, and if the heart is removed from the body, it can beat for hours without stimulation from the outside. This does not mean, however, that nerves are unimportant in heart function. On the contrary, the heart beat is regulated by two nerves. One, the *vagus nerve,* slows down the rate of the beats, while the other, the *accelerator nerve,* accelerates the heart beat. The function of the heart is thus determined by the balance of these two antagonistic nerves. Such double innervation, where one nerve is inhibitory and the other stimulating, is common in the internal organs that lack voluntary control.

Investigations of the function of the vagus nerve have revealed a great deal about *how* nerve impulses are transmitted to a target organ. The following experiment is so simple that a beginning student could do it with modest equipment and a little guidance. Two frog hearts are arranged as shown in Fig. 2-7 so that a salt solution flows through one and drips into the second. If the vagus of the top heart is stimulated, this heart slows down, but so does the second heart, which has no connection with the first heart except through the fluid that drips from it. This fluid, therefore, must contain a chemical substance which causes the effect. We now know that this substance is acetylcholine, $CH_3COOCH_2CH_2N(CH_3)_3OH$, and that it is released from many nerve endings when an impulse is transmitted. The substance released from the accelerator nerve is adrenalin: * $C_6H_3(OH)_2$-$CHOHCH_2NHCH_3$. Both acetylcholine and adrenaline disappear rapidly as they are destroyed by enzymes in the blood, otherwise they would accumulate and the regulatory system would break down.

ARTERIES. All blood vessels leading from the heart are called arteries, whether they contain oxygenated blood (as in the aorta) or deoxygenated blood (as in the pulmonary artery). The thick walls of arteries consist of heavy layers of elastic tissue. If an artery is opened, the blood spurts out because it is under the considerable pressure exerted by the force of the heart's contraction. Since the walls of the arteries are elastic, the entire arterial system expands as the blood is pushed into it during systole and thus helps absorb part of the rise in pressure. During diastole, the pressure is sustained by the elasticity of the arterial walls; arterial pressure, therefore, does not decrease to zero but fluctuates. In man the normal range is from about 120 mm Hg for systolic to 80 mm Hg for diastolic pressure. If the arterial walls were hard, the pressure would rise much higher during systole, as it actually does in older people whose arteries harden (arteriosclerosis).

The prerequisites for the high and sustained arterial pressure we find in the vertebrates are (a) a powerful pump, (b) elastic walls in the arterial system, and (c) a relatively high resistance to blood flow in the

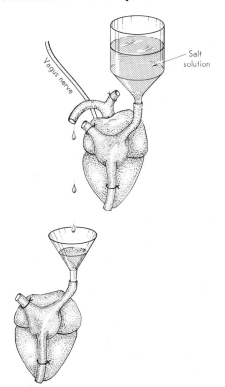

Fig. 2-7. When the vagus nerve to a frog's heart is stimulated and the heart slows down, a substance, acetylcholine, is released to the saline that flows through the heart. The presence of this substance is demonstrated as the saline flows into a second heart, which also slows down. This was the first experimental demonstration of the chemical transmission of a nerve impulse.

Salt solution

Vagus nerve

* The nerve probably releases a mixture of adrenalin and the very similar noradrenalin, $C_6H_3(OH)_2\ CHOHCH_2NH_2$.

capillaries—without this resistance (i.e., in an "open" circulatory system), even a powerful pump could not raise the pressure much. Thus, a high blood pressure is not found in invertebrates lacking a "closed" system of blood vessels.

The arteries branch as they distribute the blood to various organs. In the finest branches, the *arterioles,* which have a diameter of 0.1 mm or less, the walls are mostly muscular. Contractions and relaxations of the muscular wall change the diameter of the arterioles and therefore determine how much blood flows through them. The arterioles thus control the blood supply to the different organs, a regulation that is impossible in invertebrates with their open circulation and low blood pressure. Although the blood of an invertebrate may be efficient in acquiring oxygen, it is not nearly as effective as that of vertebrates in distributing oxygen where the demand is greatest.

CAPILLARIES. The smallest blood vessels, the capillaries, vary in size but average less than 10 µ* in diameter. Their number is very great, but they are usually not all open at the same time. In a resting muscle of a guinea pig, a cross section of one mm^2 has been found to contain about 100 open capillaries. In the working muscle, arterioles are generally open, and the blood flow increases; in a one mm^2 cross section, we could now find over 3000 open capillaries.

The capillary walls are thin, and water and dissolved substances with small molecular weight (gases, salts, sugars, amino acids, etc.) can penetrate freely and diffuse rapidly between the blood and the tissues. Molecules as large as most proteins (molecular weight of about 70,000 or larger) do not pass the capillary wall. The blood pressure, therefore, causes water and dissolved substances to seep or "filter" out of the capillary, while proteins remain in the capillary and produce an osmotic effect that attracts water. Since the small dissolved molecules pass freely, we can disregard them and consider our system to consist of a semipermeable membrane (the capillary wall), a nondiffusible but osmotically active substance inside (protein), and water outside (see p. 48). The osmotic concentration of the plasma proteins (the *colloidal osmotic pressure*) corresponds to a pressure of about 25 mm Hg—i.e., if the blood pressure in the capillary is higher than 25 mm Hg, water is forced out, but if the pressure is less than that, water is pulled in again because of the osmotic effect of the proteins. (If plasma proteins were absent, any pressure in the capillary, however low, would cause fluid to filter out, but the presence of the proteins checks the unlimited loss of fluid.)

The pressure in the capillary varies with the changing diameter of the arterioles, but it is usually relatively high in the arterial end and much lower in the venous end. In Fig. 2-8, the high pressure of 40 mm Hg in the beginning of the capillary exceeds the colloidal osmotic pressure of 25 mm Hg, and fluid is forced out (indicated by arrows crossing the capillary

* One µ (micron) is 0.001 mm.

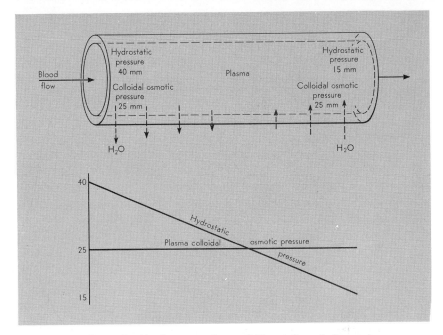

Fig. 2-8. In a capillary, the blood pressure forces fluid out through the semi-permeable wall. This filtration, however, is opposed by the effect of the plasma proteins that cannot pass the wall and that therefore attract water osmotically. As the blood pressure decreases along the capillary, the osmotic effect of the proteins cancels the filtration pressure and, toward the venous end of the capillary, even causes an osmotic flow of fluid back into the capillary. Since the capillary wall is freely permeable to salts, the system works as if these were not present at all.

wall). As the pressure decreases along the capillary, less fluid is expelled and, eventually, when the inside pressure is less than the colloidal osmotic pressure, the process is reversed and fluid returns to the capillary.

Although the amount of fluid exchange through the capillary wall fluctuates greatly, in general outflow exceeds inflow, and the excess fluid remains in the spaces between the cells. This fluid slowly drains into a system of special vessels, the *lymph ducts,* that drain into larger ducts, which eventually open into the venous system, thus returning the fluid to the blood.

VEINS. The capillaries lead into small veins, which gradually increase in size as they join other vessels on their way back to the heart. Since the blood pressure has been greatly reduced by the flow through arterioles and capillaries, the venous pressure is relatively low; the walls of the veins are thin compared to those of the arteries and are easily compressed. Valves in the veins prevent the backflow of blood, and these valves are of particular importance in the legs, where the venous pressure is insufficient to push the blood back to the heart. The blood is raised by contractions of the leg muscles, which compress the veins and squeeze the blood up towards the heart. If you stand very still and do not use the leg muscles, this mechanism does not work, the blood accumulates in the legs, and an increased formation of lymph produces some swelling in the feet.

Determination of Metabolic Rate

The over-all exchange of materials and energy of an animal is called the *total metabolism*. The *rate of metabolism* or *metabolic rate* refers to the metabolism in a given time, for example one hour. The metabolic rate can be estimated from (a) the food consumption, (b) the energy released as heat, or (c) the amount of oxygen used in oxidation processes to obtain the energy. Although all three methods are employed, they are not equally satisfactory. The first method is cumbersome and may give misleading information. If an animal starves for a few days, its food intake is zero, but metabolic processes continue and body substance is used. If, on the other hand, the food intake is high, the excess may be deposited as fat, and again the quantity of food is not a measure of turnover. The second method, heat production, is technically difficult to carry out, but is nevertheless the most accurate method of determining energy metabolism.

The determination of oxygen consumption—the third method—however, is technically easy, gives good results, and, in fact, has been used so much that when we say metabolic rate we usually mean rate of oxygen consumption. A simple apparatus for determining oxygen consumption appears in Fig. 2-9. As oxygen is used by the animal, the volume of air in the jar decreases, for the CO_2 is absorbed by alkali (NaOH) or soda lime as fast as it is formed. The movement of the drop in the graduated pipette shows the reduction in volume, and by timing its movement we get the number of ml oxygen used per minute.

Metabolic Rate in Various Animals

If we wish to compare the metabolic rates of two animals of different size, it is obvious that we must somehow take the size difference into consideration. The easiest way is to relate the oxygen consumption to body weight and

Fig. 2-9. The rate of oxygen consumption of an animal can readily be determined by using a simple apparatus constructed from material at hand. This suggested set-up will work quite well for small animals in short experiments.

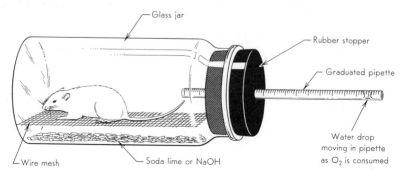

Glass jar

Rubber stopper

Graduated pipette

Water drop moving in pipette as O_2 is consumed

Wire mesh

Soda lime or NaOH

Table 2-2

OXYGEN CONSUMPTION IN VARIOUS ANIMALS AT REST

Animal	mm³/gram body wt. per hour
Sea anemone	13
Sandworm	30
Octopus	80
Squid	320
Eel	128
Trout	226
Frog	150
Man	200
Mouse	1,500
Hummingbird (rest)	3,500
Hummingbird (flight)	40,000

give the amount of oxygen used per gram body weight in a given time, for example one hour. The metabolic rates for a number of animals, expressed in this manner, are given in Table 2-2.

We all realize that, in work or activity, the need for food and oxygen increases. In order to compare different animals, therefore, we must also examine them under comparable states of activity. The simplest way is to compare them in the resting condition, for this tells us what it costs to keep the normal body processes going. The enormous amount of extra energy required for activity is clear from the change in the metabolic rate of the hummingbird in flight, indicated on the last line of Table 2-2. In a man who performs work at his maximum capacity the increase is also about 12 to 15 times the resting metabolic rate.

Our list plainly reveals that there is a great deal of variation in metabolic rates from one animal to another. In general, the highly organized and most active animals have the highest metabolic rates. If we compare related animals, such as the octopus and the squid, the complexity of their organization is found to be similar, but the squid, which is an active swimmer, has a much higher metabolic rate than the octopus, which crawls on the bottom. A similar difference is found between the two kinds of fish listed, the relatively slow-moving eel and the fast-swimming trout. Some of the highest metabolic rates observed have been found in flying birds and insects.

Metabolic Rate in Relation to Body Size

The rate of metabolic processes changes with temperature, because most body processes are speeded up with increasing temperature. We shall discuss this subject in some detail in Chapter 3; for the moment, we shall only stress that when we compare the metabolic activities of two cold-blooded animals, the observations should be made at comparable temperatures. Warm-blooded animals (mammals and birds), on the other hand, maintain a high and almost constant body temperature, and we can therefore compare their metabolic rates directly, without reference to environmental temperature.

Such comparison reveals an interesting relationship. The smaller the animal, the higher is the metabolic rate (Table 2-3). If these figures are plotted on a graph where both abscissa and ordinate are on a logarithmic scale, we find that the points fall on a straight line (Fig. 2-10). If we compare animals within other groups—crabs, for example—we find a similar

Table 2-3

THE METABOLIC RATES OF MAMMALS OF VARIOUS BODY SIZE

Animal	Body weight (grams)	Oxygen consumption (mm³/gram hour)
Mouse	25	1,580
Rat	226	872
Rabbit	2,200	466
Dog	11,700	318
Man	70,000	202
Horse	700,000	106
Elephant	3,800,000	67

Fig. 2-10. The metabolic rate of animals, calculated per gram body weight, increases with diminishing size in such a fashion that we obtain a straight line if the observations are plotted on logarithmic coordinates.

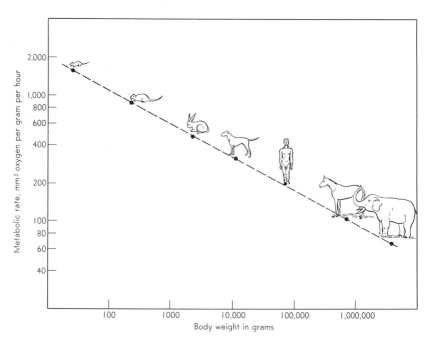

relationship between small individuals with higher metabolic rates and large individuals with lower metabolic rates. Indeed, this relationship is so common among animals, and even among plants, that it has been considered a general biological rule.

From Fig. 2-10, which shows that the metabolic rate (per gram body weight) invariably increases with diminishing body size, we suspect that there should be a minimum limit on the size of mammals, for the high metabolic rate requires a correspondingly high food intake and rapid digestion, respiration, circulation, and heart function. The smallest existing mammals are the shrews, which may have a body weight of as little as 4 grams, and their metabolic rate is, in fact, very high. A shrew has to eat almost constantly and is always on the lookout for food. It must eat nearly its own body weight of food per day, and if deprived of food, the high metabolic rate consumes the body reserves so fast that in a few hours it starves to death. If a mammal were even smaller, it would have to eat at such a tremendous rate and spend so much effort looking for food that it simply could not exist. We can conclude, therefore, that there is a lower theoretical limit to the size of mammals.

If we look at the opposite extreme of our curve, we can readily see that the elephant could not possibly maintain a metabolic rate comparable to that of the shrew. He would have to eat huge quantities of plant material and tear through the forest like a hurricane, gobbling leaves and branches at a tremendous rate. But, since metabolic rate actually decreases with increasing body size, the limit to the body size of mammals is not set by the requirements for food. Land animals cannot increase to unlimited size because the mechanical strength of their muscles and bones could not support their enormous weight. The heavy bones and thick legs of the rhinoceros and the elephant are evidence of the strength needed to support a large body; a further increase in weight is just not possible, for the animal would become overly cumbersome. The giant dinosaurs that lived in earlier geological periods were semi-aquatic and lived in swamps, so part of their body weight was supported by water. Some of them probably weighed 40 to 50 tons, and they must have been almost helpless on land. The largest living land mammal, the elephant, only weighs about 4 tons, but the largest animal that has ever lived, the blue whale, is completely aquatic and so can maneuver despite its 80- or 100-ton bulk.

Temperature

C H A P T E R   T H R E E

Active animal life is restricted to a narrow range of temperature of some 50°C, from a low limit of about −1°C, the temperature of Arctic waters, to an upper limit of about 50°C, the temperature of some hot springs in which a few animals are able to live. Compared to the wide range of cosmic temperatures, this is a very narrow range indeed. Such livable temperatures exist, however, over most of the surface of the earth and throughout the oceans, at least during part of the year.

In relation to temperature, animals are of two types, cold-blooded and warm-blooded. The majority are cold-blooded but mammals and birds are warm-blooded. These terms are quite misleading, and it is necessary to clarify what they mean. The cold-blooded animal is not necessarily cold, but it has about the same temperature as its surroundings: An earthworm has the temperature of the soil it lives in, a fish the temperature of the water it swims in. If the temperature of the surroundings changes, so does the body temperature of the animal. The scientific term, *poikilothermic animal,* is really more descriptive, for it signifies changeable temperature.

Mammals and birds are called *homothermic* (which is a better expression than "warm-blooded") because they maintain a quite constant body temperature in spite of wide variations in their surroundings. Thus, a tropical monkey, a polar bear, and a walrus have the same body temperature of about 38°C.

Within the temperature range that permits an active and normal life for a poikilothermic animal, *temperature change* has a profound effect on metabolic processes. Furthermore, many animals will tolerate temperatures below the limit for active life and survive cold in an inactive, or torpid, condition. The tolerance to high temperatures, on the other hand, is usually quite limited, although some organisms are more tolerant to heat than others, particularly in the resting stage. Organisms such as bacterial spores, for example, may be tolerant to temperatures above 120°C.

Homothermic animals maintain a constant body temperature by *temperature regulation* and remain active in hot as well as cold surroundings. To escape the effects of extreme seasonal cold and food shortage, however, some mammals and a few birds *hibernate* through the winter, at which time they experience a profound drop in body temperature.

POIKILOTHERMIC ANIMALS

Variation in Metabolic Rate with Temperature

As we have seen, all animals, except mammals and birds, are poikilothermic and have body temperatures which fluctuate with that of the surroundings. This does not mean that they cannot control their temperature at all, for they can seek out warm or cold spots in the environment, but they do lack the extensive physiological mechanisms employed by the homotherms to maintain a virtually constant body temperature.

Within the temperature range that can be tolerated by a poikilotherm, the rate of metabolism (and that of many other processes) increases with increasing temperature, and in a fairly regular manner. Often the rate about doubles for a temperature rise of ten degrees, which, if the increase continues over a wide range, is a rapidly accelerating pace. Suppose we have an animal that can tolerate the entire temperature range from zero to 40°C and that has a rate which doubles with each increase of 10°. If in Fig. 3-1 we graph the metabolic rate against the temperature, we see that an increase from 30° to 40° is as great as the total increase from 0° to 30°. The increase in rate for each 10° temperature rise is called Q_{10}. If the rate is doubled, Q_{10} is 2, and if the rate is tripled for each 10° rise, Q_{10} is 3, etc. The type of curve we obtain is called an exponential curve, for it is mathematically described by an exponential function:

$$M_2 = M_1 \cdot Q_{10}^{(T_2 - T_1)/10}$$

where M_2 and M_1 are the metabolic rates at two temperatures, T_2 and

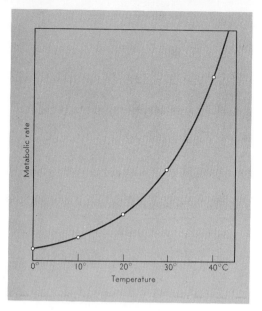

Fig. 3-1. If the metabolic rate of an animal doubles with a ten degree rise in temperature, the rate will increase more and more rapidly, as shown by the rising curve. This type of curve, which is called an exponential curve, is characteristic of many processes in living organisms.

T_1. This general equation permits us to calculate the Q_{10} when observations have been made at two temperatures that are not ten degrees apart.*

It is interesting that many chemical processes are dependent on temperature in a similar way; that is, they have a Q_{10} of about 2 to 3. In particular, many enzymatic reactions are accelerated at this rate by increased temperatures. Since the enzymes are catalysts of organic origin, this is not surprising, but it bears out the great similarity in the nature of chemical processes inside the body and outside.

Effects of Heat and Lethal Temperatures

The highest body temperature that can be tolerated by animals varies, but a great many terrestrial animals, mammals, birds, reptiles, and insects have a lethal limit of around 45°C. The highest tolerance to temperature is found in animals that live in hot springs, where protozoans and mosquito larvae have been found thriving at 50°C. In general, aquatic animals have a lower tolerance than land animals, and many die at 35°C or 30°C. Some arctic animals, which normally live in water close to freezing, may die if the temperature is raised to only 10°C. Since the lethal temperature depends not only on the temperature but also on the duration of exposure to the extreme temperature, to be precise we must specify the exposure time for any given lethal temperature.

Although some factors about heat death are understood, its exact cause remains obscure. We know that proteins coagulate and become denatured at high temperature, about 50°C and higher, and that enzymes (which are proteins) are inactivated. This inactivation frequently begins somewhere above 40°C and proceeds more rapidly with increasing temperature. Since

* The mathematical treatment of an exponential function becomes quite easy if we use the logarithmic form of the equation. In our case, this would be:

$$\log M_2 = \log M_1 + \frac{T_2 - T_1}{10} \log Q_{10}$$

A number of rate processes are described by exponential equations, such as acceleration, growth curves, radio-active decay, etc.

the inactivation of an enzyme is also a function of time, we can readily understand that a longer exposure to high temperature is less well tolerated by an animal than a short exposure. If the thermal destruction of proteins and enzymes goes beyond a certain point, even a return to lower temperature will not help. On the other hand, the heat death of an arctic fish at 10°C cannot easily be explained by denaturation of enzymes. It may be that death in this case is due to an increase in the need for oxygen, or some other metabolic process, which cannot be met.

Effects of Cold

As the temperature of an organism decreases, the speed of physiological processes diminishes; oxygen consumption goes down, movements are slower, and the animal becomes lethargic or torpid. It is in this state of cold torpor that poikilothermic animals pass the winter at high latitudes. Further cooling may be fatal to an animal, but the degree of cooling that can be tolerated is extremely variable. Many tropical fish kept by aquarium hobbyists will not thrive unless the water is heated above room temperature, and if the heat is off on a cool night they simply die, in contrast to arctic fish that live and thrive in water close to 0°C.

Many animals will even tolerate a temperature drop to below freezing, although extensive freezing with actual ice formation in the tissues is fatal to most animals. This is not always so, however. Mosquito larvae, which in Alaska normally pass the winter frozen in the ice of water pools, are known to tolerate repeated freezings and thawings. It is very easy to determine the extent of ice formation by determining the change in specific gravity upon freezing, for ice is 10 per cent lighter than water. With this method, it has been found that 90 per cent of the water in the mosquito larva freezes to ice at −15°C. Many lower organisms have been cooled in liquid oxygen to a temperature of −183°C and in liquid helium to −269°C and have survived. Why freezing can be tolerated by some animals and not by others is very difficult to understand. That the growth of ice crystals in a cell would disrupt its finer structure seems only natural, but why is it not so in all animals? And why is the disorganization in some animals irreversible at temperatures far above the freezing point?

Acclimation to High and Low Temperatures

Animals can to some extent get used to, or acclimate to, extreme temperatures, but this ability is not unlimited. Even with a very slow increase in temperature, we reach an absolute upper lethal limit for a particular animal beyond which it cannot adjust to a further increase. Similarly, the absolute lower lethal limit is that point beyond which no further decrease in temperature is tolerated.

A picture of the complete thermal range of an animal can be conveniently presented in the form of a graph like the one in Fig. 3-2, which shows

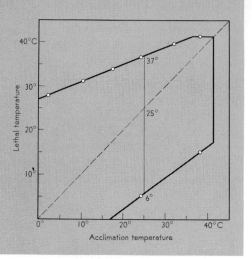

Fig. 3-2. The thermal tolerance of a goldfish is described in this graph, which shows that if the goldfish is kept at some temperature on the dashed line until it has become adjusted, or acclimated, its tolerance to heat can be read on the upper solid line, and the tolerance to cold on the lower solid line. For example, if the fish is acclimated at 25°C, its upper lethal limit will be 37°C and its lower lethal limit 6°C. (From F. E. J. Fry, et al., Revue Canadienne de Biologie, 1, 1942.)

the thermal acclimation of goldfish. The upper lethal temperature is 27°C for fish kept at 0°C, and increases to 41°C for fish kept at 36°C. The goldfish could not adjust to higher temperatures than 41°C, even if kept above 36°C, say at 39°C. The lower lethal limit is 0°C (or slightly below) for fish kept in water up to 17°C, but if they are acclimated at higher temperatures, the lower lethal limit rises. For goldfish kept in the warmest water they can tolerate, the lower lethal limit is 17°C.

The thermal tolerance is not the same in other fishes, and the polygon that describes the thermal tolerance will therefore look different. For a cold-water fish such as the speckled trout, the thermal tolerance is much less, and the total area covered by the polygon is only half that of the goldfish. In other animals, it is different still; in many tropical fish the entire tolerance range is in the upper part of the wide range tolerated by the goldfish.

Temperature Regulation in Poikilotherms

Although the temperature of cold-blooded animals follows that of the surroundings more or less passively, this does not mean that the animal has no control whatever over its body temperature. By seeking out environments with certain temperatures, the animal can to a great extent influence its temperature and thus, too, its level of activity. Snakes and lizards will often be found basking in the sun in the early morning hours; the radiation from the sun makes their temperature rise above that of the surroundings. Later in the day, they will keep out of the sun, and on a hot day they will hide under rocks or in cool burrows. The behavior of a desert lizard keeps it from getting overheated, for its lethal temperature is similar to that of other lizards, about 45°C, and it will die if kept for ten or fifteen minutes in the open sun.

Insects have a special thermal problem because of their high rate of metabolism during flight. If an insect is too cold, its muscles cannot contract fast enough to carry it in flight, but it can increase the temperature of the flight muscles considerably by contractions similar to shivering in man. On a cool day, you can sometimes see butterflies with spread-out wings vibrating for several minutes before they take off. When the actual temperature in the muscles of the butterfly's wings was measured with fine thermocouples, it was found that this warm-up period, when the air was 20°C, increased the muscle temperature to 35°C in six minutes. Thus, some cold-blooded animals are able to regulate actively their body temperature to suit their physiological needs.

HOMOTHERMIC ANIMALS

Temperature Regulation

As we know, mammals and birds maintain an almost constant body temperature. In man, for example, the normal body temperature is about 37°C, with a slight decrease at night and a slight increase in daytime, amounting to a diurnal change of about 1°C. If the body temperature is only a few degrees higher it is a serious fever, and if a few degrees lower the body suffers a dangerous degree of cooling. The variation in body temperature from species to species is not great, a few degrees at most. A mouse has a normal body temperature of 36.5°C, a horse 37.7°C, and an elephant 36.2°C. In general, the body temperature of birds is a little higher, in the range of 40°C to 43°C.

MAN. As an example of temperature regulation in a homotherm, let us look at the situation in man. The diagram in Fig. 3-3 depicts the reactions of a man at rest who is subjected to varying temperatures. In the narrow range between 27°C and 31°C, he will feel comfortable, his body temperature will not change, and the heat produced in metabolism is given off to the surroundings. If the room is cooler than 27°C, his body loses heat faster than it is produced, and the only way he can maintain his body temperature is to produce more heat, which is done by involuntary muscle contractions which we call shivering. The colder it is, the more heat he must produce to keep up with the rate of cooling and thus the more he shivers. If the temperature is higher than 31°C, the air is not sufficiently

Fig. 3-3. A nude man at rest will shiver in a room colder than 27°C, and the lower the temperature the more he will shiver. If the temperature is above 31°C he will sweat but, in the narrow range of thermoneutrality between 27°C and 31°C, his body temperature can be controlled without either shivering or sweating. Work or clothing changes the range of thermoneutrality downwards, i.e., we can keep warm at lower temperatures without shivering if we work or use more clothes.

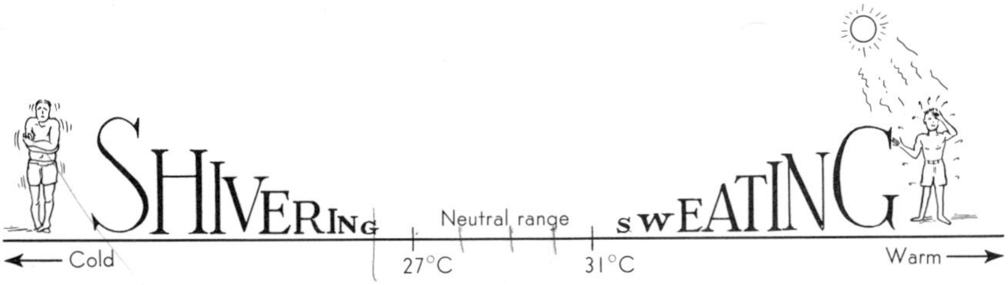

SHIVERINg   Neutral range   swEATING

← Cold   27°C   31°C   Warm →

cool to remove the heat produced in metabolism, and the only way he can cool the body is to evaporate water by sweating. The hotter the room, the more he must sweat.

Thus man has a narrow range of thermoneutrality between 27°C and 31°C. This range of thermoneutrality does not hold if we wear clothing. In the cold, we insulate the body surface and keep from shivering. In warm surroundings, of course, clothes cut down the heat loss, and we sweat more readily or remove the clothing. So far we have not discussed what occurs within the range of thermoneutrality. Toward the lower end of the range, the body attempts to cut down the heat loss by reducing the amount of blood circulating to the skin, while toward the upper end as much blood as possible is sent to the skin to become cooled. Inside the range, this mechanism suffices to adjust the rate of heat loss to heat production; outside the range, as we have seen, shivering or sweating has to be employed.

OTHER MAMMALS. In other mammals, a varying amount of fur gives them a range of thermoneutrality different from that of man. The insulation is particularly important to arctic animals, for if they had to maintain heat balance by increased metabolism in the cold, the cost in food would be tremendous. The Alaskan ground squirrel has a lower limit of thermo-neutrality of about 10°C; below this, it must increase its metabolism to maintain a high body temperature. An Eskimo husky, however, has much heavier fur, and he takes full advantage of it when he curls up in the snow and goes to sleep. He is so well insulated that his metabolism increases only when the temperature drops below −30°C.

The arctic seals have a somewhat different problem. When they swim in water close to 0°C, the wet fur is very poor protection against heat loss, and, accordingly, most of the insulation is under the skin in the heavy layer of blubber. The fur, however, is still needed, for seals and walruses leave the water to rest on the ice, and without the fur the outer part of the skin would be damaged in subfreezing temperatures. Whales also depend on their heavy layer of blubber for insulation, and since they are completely aquatic, hair is superfluous and the skin is hairless.

THE TEMPERATURE-REGULATING CENTER IN MAN. The regulation of body temperature is very precise and is controlled from the hypothalamus located at the base of the brain. If the body needs more heat, the hypothala-mus sends nerve impulses to the muscles, causing contractions and shiver-ing. If the body needs cooling, impulses to the sweat glands induce sweat production. If the hypothalamus is cooled locally, shivering starts immedi-ately. The temperature-regulating center, therefore, acts much like the thermostat in a house. Normally, if the house gets cooler, the thermostat turns the heater on, and if we cool the thermostat only, the heat comes on as if the whole house were too cold.

PANTING. The temperature-regulating center in other homotherms works much like the one in man. Cooling of the body is counteracted by increased heat production, and overheating is prevented by evaporation of water. Not all animals produce sweat, however—a dog, for example, sweats scarcely at all. Instead, water is evaporated from the tongue and upper respiratory tract, and the evaporation is facilitated by an extremely rapid rate of respiration, called *panting,* which increases the passage of air over the wet surfaces. The normal rate of respiration in a dog is some 15 to 30 breaths per minute, but in panting this rate rises to over 300 per minute.

The very rapid respiratory rate is only partly offset by a reduction in the depth of breathing, and panting therefore results in a greatly increased exchange of air in the lungs. This causes a correspondingly excessive removal of carbon dioxide from the blood. Not only does the panting continue in spite of the decrease in the normal stimulus to respiration (CO_2) but a dog can tolerate a depletion of carbon dioxide that in man would produce loss of consciousness and severe cramps and might cause death. The panting in the dog is as efficient a way of cooling the body as sweating in man. Cattle and sheep both sweat and pant, but not as efficiently as man and dog.

A third mechanism for cooling is utilized by kangaroos and to some extent by rabbits and cats. When they get overheated, they wet down the fur of the limbs and belly by licking them and are thus cooled by the evaporation of the moisture. This method, however, is not as efficient as sweating or panting.

Cooling by evaporation dehydrates the body. Small animals have a large relative surface, which means that in hot surroundings they will heat up faster than a large animal of greater bulk. Since, in addition, their metabolic heat production is also higher, the cost of heat regulation becomes too great to be tolerated. Accordingly, we find that small animals, such as rodents, have no true sweat glands and do not pant; instead, they avoid the heat by living in underground burrows.

TEMPERATURE REGULATION IN BIRDS. Birds have no sweat glands. They could not possibly evolve sweating as a cooling mechanism and still fly, for if they had to evaporate water from their skin, the air between the feathers would have to be renewed rapidly. In flight, then, the air flow over the surface of the feathers could not be smooth and streamlined but would be turbulent and thereby cause a considerable drag on the flight. Accordingly, birds do not sweat.

Some birds do, to some extent, increase the rate of respiration, similarly to the panting of dogs. It has also been suggested that the extensive air-sac system connected with the lungs may be important in temperature regulation, but such a function of the air-sacs lacks experimental support. How birds dissipate the large amounts of heat produced in flight is a mystery that awaits investigation for no physiologist has yet successfully studied this problem.

Hibernation

Animals that pass the winter in a lethargic or tropid state are commonly said to hibernate, but the physiologist applies a more precise definition to this condition. He defines the hibernation of warm-blooded animals as a state in which the body temperature is greatly decreased and the metabolism, respiration, heart rate, etc., are considerably reduced. Mammals that hibernate belong to three orders—insectivores, bats, and rodents —and include, among others, woodchucks, hamsters, hedgehogs, ground squirrels, and many bats. Bears are not considered true hibernators, for although they sleep through a major part of the winter, their body temperature does not decrease more than a few degrees. The bear thus maintains a relatively high metabolic rate and can be awakened without going through a long period of rewarming, as was demonstrated when a physiologist in Alaska entered the den of a hibernating bear and was prevented from measuring its rectal temperature because the sleepy and grumbling bear sat down on its tail like a dog. In contrast, a hibernating hamster or bat is completely torpid.

The state of hibernation allows an animal to remain dormant during winter when food is less readily available and the maintenance of a normal body temperature would require a high metabolic rate. A large animal, such as a bear, which normally has a relatively low metabolic rate, can lie down in a den and sleep through months while it slowly uses up its reserves of fat. A small animal, on the other hand, has such a high metabolic rate that it could not live on its reserves for more than a few days, or weeks at best, if it were to maintain a normal metabolic rate. If the body temperature is permitted to drop, however, the metabolic rate decreases to a small fraction of normal, and the animal can survive the winter on its reserves.

The hibernator is in a state comparable to that of a cold-blooded animal. Its body temperature is close to that of the surroundings and rises and falls with it, but if the temperature increases appreciably, the animal warms up again and returns to the warm-blooded state. During hibernation the oxygen consumption may drop to $1/30$ to $1/100$ of the normal, the heart rate goes down to a few beats per minute, and the respiratory movements become very slow. It may appear that the major change in a hibernator is the failure of the temperature-regulating center, but this is not the case, for it has been found in some hibernators that if the temperature sinks to below freezing, heat production in the animal increases to prevent its tissues from freezing. Extreme cold weather may even stimulate full awakening. Thus, the hibernator does not behave as a poikilotherm—hibernation is a well-regulated physiological state that permits survival during the most unfavorable part of the year.

The bats differ from other hibernators in that they do not restrict "hibernation" to the winter. In summer, when they rest during the day, their body temperature decreases to the ambient temperature. Thus, they behave as hibernators every day, and the long winter sleep can be considered as an extension of their daily sleep.

HIBERNATION IN BIRDS.   Until recently it was believed that only mammals were hibernators, but during a field trip in the California deserts, a biology class discovered a torpid desert poorwill in a rock crevice. Returning weeks later, they found the bird in the same position, and when they measured its body temperature they confirmed that it was in a state of hibernation. Hummingbirds experience a nocturnal temperature drop similar to the diurnal drop in bats. These small birds weigh only a few grams and have a very high metabolic rate. They feed in the daytime, mostly on flower nectar, and when they rest for the night, their body temperature drops, carrying the metabolic rate with it. Without such a decrease in metabolism, the hummingbird would be in the same situation as the shrew and use up all its reserves in a single night.

HEAT EXCHANGERS—HOW WHALES KEEP WARM.   A whale that swims in the chilly waters of the Antarctic maintains the same body temperature as other mammals, nearly 40°C, although it is constantly immersed in ice water. The body surface is insulated by a thick layer of blubber but the flippers and the tail fluke are thin-skinned and poorly insulated. In fact, these surfaces seem particularly well suited for dissipating heat, for they receive a rich blood supply. If all the blood that gets cooled in these thin structures were returned to the body at a temperature approaching freezing, the heat loss from the body would be excessive. However, the blood vessels in the fluke and flippers are arranged so that they function as excellent heat exchangers. Each artery is actually surrounded by veins (see Fig. 3-4A), an arrangement that results in a transfer of heat from the artery

Fig. 3-4. (A) Blood vessels in a porpoise fluke. (B) A counter-current heat exchanger permits the return to the furnace of part of the heat otherwise lost with the exhaust fumes. (C) Diagrammatic representation of the shift in venous blood flow in the arm of man from superficial vessels in warm surroundings to deep-lying vessels in the cold. ((A) from P. F. Scholander and William E. Schevill, "Counter-current vascular heat exchange in the fins of whales," J. Appl. Physiol., **8**, 279–282, 1955.)

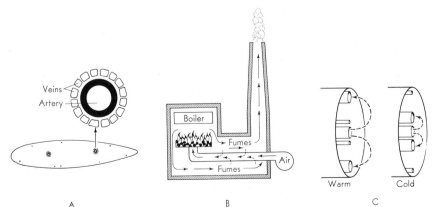

A   B   C

to the veins, thus preheating the chilled blood before it returns to the body. Similar heat exchangers are widely used in industrial processes, such as heating plants, distillation, pasteurization of milk, etc. (see Fig. 3-4B). In the whale's appendages it serves to remove heat from the arterial blood and return it to the body via the venous blood.

The diagram indicates in schematic fashion how the heat exchange takes place. As warm blood passes through the artery it is surrounded by cooler venous blood and by conduction it gives up part of its heat. Before it reaches the peripheral capillary circulation it has been precooled almost to the temperature of the surrounding water and therefore can lose practically no heat. Almost all the heat lost from the artery goes to reheat venous blood and is therefore returned to the body, and only a minor amount is lost to the surrounding water.

It is important to note that this type of counter-current heat exchanger depends only on the simple conduction of heat from a higher to a lower temperature, and that the effect depends entirely on the structural arrangement of the blood vessels.

Similar counter-current heat exchangers exist in other animals, and to some extent also in man. The arteries to our arms and legs are located deep in the tissues, each with an adjacent pair of veins (Fig. 3-4C). In cold surroundings most of the venous blood returns in these veins and is therefore preheated by the artery before entering the main body; in warmer surroundings the major part of the blood returns in surface veins under the skin and is thus diverted from the heat exchanger. The arterial blood then reaches the periphery without being precooled, and more heat can be dissipated. You can actually observe this change on your own forearm where the surface veins under the skin are much more prominent in warm surroundings.

Water

CHAPTER FOUR

Water is essential to life, and animals must maintain a high and rather constant water content in order to survive. Water is the general solvent in the body and the medium for virtually all metabolic processes. If it is withdrawn from the organism, most animals soon succumb, but a few can tolerate a considerable water loss and still live in a "resting stage" with greatly reduced metabolic activity. As a rule of thumb, we can say that the body weight of most animals is two-thirds water, although the percentage varies widely (see Table 4-1).

All cells and body fluids contain dissolved salts in concentrations that usually remain quite constant. The commonest *cations* are sodium and potassium, and the commonest *anions* are chloride, bicarbonate, and phosphate. Many physiological functions are quite sensitive to the concentrations and the relative amounts of ions; for example, the heart will stop if there is a small increase in the potassium concentration of the blood, and a small increase in magnesium will block nerve function and thus act as an anesthetic (magnesium salts have actually been used for anesthesia).

The problems that animals encounter in their attempt to

Table 4-1

WATER CONTENT OF VARIOUS ANIMALS

Animal	Percentage of body weight
Mammals, total body	65
(blood 83%)	
(brain 80%)	
(muscle 75%)	
(skin 70%)	
(bone 30%)	
(fat 10%)	
Chicken	74
Frog	78
Codfish	82
Herring	67
Lobster	79
Jellyfish	95
Earthworm	80
Blowfly	79
Cockroach	61
Flour beetle	59
Bean weevil	48

maintain a relatively constant composition are rather different if they live in the sea, with its 3½ per cent salt content, in fresh water, which is almost salt free, or on land, where water evaporates and the animal is in danger of desiccation. We shall therefore discuss these three environments separately on the basis of the physiological problems each poses.

WATER, DISSOLVED SUBSTANCES, AND OSMOSIS

In order to understand physiological reactions, however, we must have some knowledge of the behavior of substances in solution. If a soluble substance—for example, sugar—is placed on the bottom of a beaker of water and left without stirring, the sugar will gradually dissolve and diffuse throughout the water until it is evenly distributed in the entire volume. A dissolved substance always tends to diffuse from a higher to a lower concentration, and an equilibrium is reached when the concentration is equal throughout. Since this equilibrium results from simple physical laws that are similar to the gas laws, the even distribution of sugar molecules in our example is comparable to the even distribution of gas molecules in an enclosed space.

Suppose we look at our system from the viewpoint of water concentration. Where the sugar concentration is high, water is present in lower concentration than in pure water, and water will diffuse from a point where its concentration is high to where it is low (sugar high). We rarely look at water concentration in this way, but it is helpful to realize that both dissolved material and solvent tend to diffuse from higher to lower concentrations.

By a simple experiment, we can imitate part of the behavior of most living cells. We enclose some sugar solution in a cellophane bag, which can be a piece of sausage tubing tied at each end by a knot, and put this bag into pure water. Since the cellophane is permeable to both water and sugar, water will immediately start diffusing into the bag, while sugar will diffuse out of the bag. In the beginning, the water will diffuse in faster than the sugar diffuses out, for small molecules diffuse faster than large ones, but at the end, when equilibrium has been reached, the sugar will be evenly distributed in all the water, inside and outside the bag. If the solu-

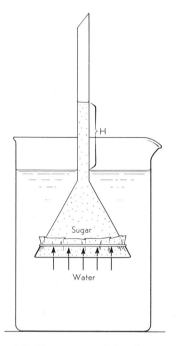

H

Sugar

Water

Fig. 4-1. If a sugar solution is separated from pure water by a membrane that is permeable to water but not to sugar, water will enter the sugar solution with a force that equals the pressure, which is indicated by the height to which the solution rises; H will increase with increasing concentration of the sugar.

tion in the bag were initially quite concentrated, however, the water would enter so fast that the bag would swell and burst.

If our bag were permeable to water and not to sugar, all the sugar would remain inside and water would continue to enter. Since our bag would then expand and burst, let us replace it by the more suitable but equally simple apparatus shown in Fig. 4-1. We will tie our cellophane over the long-stemmed funnel and insert it into water. As the water enters, the solution inside rises in the stem. At a certain level, the rise in pressure caused by the water in the stem equals the force with which the water tends to enter the sugar solution, and no more water can enter. The height of the water column, *H,* indicates this pressure, which is called the *osmotic pressure* of the solution.*

The height to which the solution rises in the tube in our apparatus (an *osmometer*) depends on how much sugar is in the solution. With twice the sugar concentration, the solution rises twice as high, and the pressure is twice as great. As it turns out, the magnitude of the osmotic pressure—or, as we frequently say, the *osmotic concentration*—depends only on the number of particles dissolved per volume, and not on their size or nature. If several different substances are dissolved, the osmotic concentration depends on the sum of all dissolved particles.

A one-molar solution of sucrose contains 342 grams of sucrose per liter, and a one-molar solution of glucose 180 grams per liter, but since they both have the same number of molecules in solution, they have the same osmotic concentration and are designated as 1-osmolar (Osm) solutions. Frequently, it is more practical to employ a smaller unit, and we then use the usual metric prefix "milli," meaning a thousandth, and designate a milliosmolar solution as 1 mOsm or 0.001 Osm. Since sodium chloride in solution dissociates into sodium ions and chloride ions, each molecule of NaCl gives rise to two separate, osmotically active particles, and a one-millimolar solution of sodium chloride thus has an osmotic concentration

* We must work with quite dilute solutions, otherwise the fluid rises and runs out the tip of the stem. It would not be practical to use a longer stem, for the pressure of a high fluid column would cause the membrane to burst.

of 2 milliosmol. (The dissociation of sodium chloride is complete only in dilute solution, and in more concentrated solutions we find osmotic activity slightly lower than expected. The deviations are of little significance to the biological work we discuss here.)

It is often impractical to use the osmometer described above to determine osmotic concentration, because this method, in spite of its theoretical simplicity, involves many difficulties, a major one being the virtual impossibility of making a truly semipermeable membrane that is permeable to water but not to solutes. However, a number of physical properties vary with the osmotic activity of dissolved substances in such a way that they can be used to determine osmotic concentration. The most commonly used methods are based on the lowering of the vapor pressure or the freezing point of solutions.

If we now return to the osmotic relations of the living cell, we can conveniently use the red blood cell as a model. The membrane of the red cell is permeable to water, but seemingly impermeable to salts. If it is placed in a solution of about 160 millimolar NaCl, which is osmotically equivalent to plasma, it retains its shape and size, but if placed in a more dilute solution, water enters and it swells. Immersed in pure water, the cell swells and bursts, and the contents spill out. If put in a more concentrated solution, water leaves the cell, and it shrinks. This behavior of the red blood cell is a good illustration of how animals react in water, as we shall discuss in the next few pages.

AQUATIC ANIMALS

Marine Invertebrates

Most invertebrates that live in the sea have an osmotic concentration in their body fluids which equals that of the surrounding sea water. Although the total osmotic concentration in the body fluids and tissues equals that of the sea water, the relative abundance of the salts is not the same. Since the surface of an animal is never completely impermeable to salts (in particular, the gills may be relatively permeable), the difference in salt concentration must be maintained by means of an active regulation. This is called *ionic regulation* to distinguish it from the osmoregulation discussed in the next paragraph.

When a marine invertebrate is placed in dilute sea water, the higher osmotic concentration in the animal will initially cause water to enter the animal, but after a period of adjustment it settles again into equilibrium with its new environment. Most animals that are strictly marine can tolerate only a limited change in the concentration of the sea water, and if it becomes too dilute they die. With changes in the salinity of the water, the osmotic concentration of the animal also changes, as is shown in Fig. 4-2 for a spider crab (*Maia*).

If we look instead at the shore crab (*Carcinus*), we find that it can actively resist changes in its osmotic concentration; it has the power of *osmoregulation*. Carcinus can live in brackish water; in normal sea water it is in osmotic equilibrium, but in dilute sea water it maintains a higher osmotic concentration in the blood than that in the surrounding water (see Fig. 4-2). In this situation, the internal osmotic concentration in the crab causes a steady inflow of water, which must be eliminated again. Since the crab has a kidney (actually the green gland or antennary gland), the water can be excreted, but the curious fact is that the urine formed is not dilute but has the same osmotic concentration as the blood (is *isotonic* with the blood). This process will eliminate the water, but it does not help maintain a high salt concentration in the crab; this would be accomplished only if the urine were more dilute. The problem is solved by the

Fig. 4-2. The osmotic concentration in the blood of marine invertebrates varies with the concentration in the water. The 45° dotted line indicates equal concentrations in blood and water. In a strictly marine species—here the spider crab —the blood concentration equals the concentration in the water. The shore crab, which can tolerate brackish water, can maintain a blood concentration above that in the water, but in very dilute water its osmoregulation breaks down and the animal dies. The mitten crab has a more efficient osmoregulatory mechanism, can penetrate into fresh water, and can also, at high salt concentration, maintain a lower concentration in the blood than that in the water. (The concentration of sea water is about 500mM.)

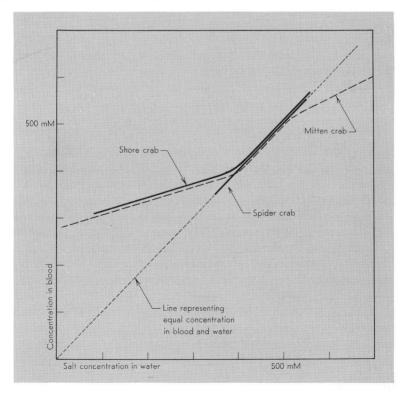

gill's ability to secrete salt into the blood, thus removing ions from the water and moving them into the more concentrated blood. The salt naturally tends to diffuse in the opposite direction, from the concentrated blood to the more dilute water, and the transport is therefore against the concentration gradient, requires energy, and is called *active transport*.

The ability of a marine animal to penetrate into a brackish or estuarine environment depends on three different abilities, or a combination of them: (a) The animal may temporarily exclude dilute sea water—for example, a clam or oyster may close its shells when the changing tides bring highly diluted sea water; (b) the animal may be tolerant to the decrease that occurs in the concentration of its body fluids as the salinity of the water decreases temporarily; (c) the animal may, as we saw in the shore crab, actively take up salt from the water and maintain a higher osmotic concentration than the surrounding water. This form of osmotic regulation will enable the efficient animal to live in quite dilute water, and may even permit him to penetrate into fresh water. The Chinese mitten crab (*Eriocheir*) can live in the rivers of Central Europe, but it must return to the sea to breed, for the eggs do not tolerate fresh water. This crab, then, shows the transition in osmoregulation that is necessary for life in fresh water.

Marine animals placed in more concentrated sea water will usually show increased blood concentrations equal to that of the water, but some, including the mitten crab, can maintain concentrations lower than the surrounding water by actively transporting salt from the blood to the water. Such regulation becomes particularly important in animals, such as the fairy shrimp, *Artemia,* that live in salt lakes. *Artemia* can exist in salt solutions containing as little as 0.26 per cent NaCl and in concentrated brine containing as much as 30 per cent salt. The osmotic concentration of the blood is relatively independent of the medium and increases only slightly as the salt content of the water increases.

Marine Fishes

The bony fishes (teleosts) in the sea are not in equilibrium, for they maintain an osmotic concentration of about one-third that of sea water. Since they are not impermeable, they lose water to the more concentrated sea water and are actually in constant danger of dehydration. They compensate for the water loss by drinking sea water, and both water and salt are absorbed from the intestine (Fig. 4-3). The fish kidney is unable to produce a concentrated urine to help eliminate the salt; instead, the gills secrete the excess salt into the sea water. Since this secretion is from a lower concentration in the blood to a higher one outside, it is an active transport and requires energy.

The elasmobranch fishes (sharks and rays) have solved their osmotic problem in an entirely different way. Their salt content is less than one-half that in sea water, but the blood contains such large amounts of organic

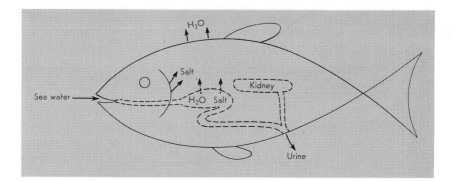

Fig. 4-3. A fish living in the sea has a steady loss of water because the salt concentration in sea water is higher than in the fish. To compensate for the water loss, the fish drinks sea water. The excess salt taken up is excreted by the gills.

compounds that the total osmotic concentration equals that of sea water. The organic compounds are primarily urea $[CO(NH_2)_2]$, which is normally excreted by the kidney in other animals but is retained by sharks, and trimethylamine oxide $[(CH_3)_3N = O]$, a compound frequently found in marine animals but whose origin and metabolism are only vaguely known. This unusual composition of the shark blood eliminates the osmotic problem of inflowing water, despite the fact that they maintain the low salt concentration which is characteristic of vertebrates in general.

Fresh-Water Animals

All fresh-water invertebrates, as well as fishes and amphibians, are hypertonic to the surrounding water. Since they are never completely impermeable, they have a steady inflow of water and some loss of salt. They eliminate the water as urine, and by forming a urine of very low concentration, they keep the salt loss in the kidney to a minimum. Some salt inevitably is lost, however, and must be made up by food or by active absorption from the very dilute water. Numerous fresh-water invertebrates can absorb salt actively, and probably all of them have some salt-absorbing mechanism. For life to evolve in fresh water, an efficient mechanism for osmotic regulation is obviously necessary. The particular mechanisms vary from group to group, and much work remains to be done in this field.

In fresh-water fishes, the water that enters the body is eliminated by the kidney. The urine is quite low in salt and is highly hypotonic, as it is in most fresh-water animals. The site of ion absorption in fish is in the gills; for the situation in fresh-water fish see Fig. 4-4. A comparison with the salt-water fish shows that when a fish, such as the salmon, migrates between salt and fresh water, it must change the direction of salt transport.

Amphibians are very similar to fresh-water fish, although the adult animals have no gills and the absorption of salt takes place from the entire skin surface. In fact, it has been found that isolated pieces of frog skin will continue to transport salt for hours if placed as a separating membrane

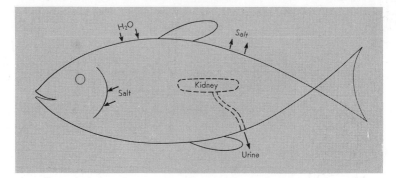

Fig. 4-4. The fresh-water fish has a higher salt concentration than the water and therefore loses salt while water enters the body. Although this exchange is pictured as taking place from the general body surface, much of it occurs in the gill, which is more permeable than the skin. Water is eliminated as urine, and the salt loss is compensated for by active absorption of salt in the gill.

between two suitable solutions. Such experiments have been widely used in the study of the ion-transport mechanism.

Amphibians are generally unable to adapt to a marine life, although there are a few exceptions. One of these, the crab-eating frog of southeast Asia, swims and seeks its food in sea water. It maintains an osmotic concentration in its body fluids similar to the water in which it swims, far above what is tolerated by other frogs. About one-half of the solutes is salt and one-half urea; thus, this frog is osmotically similar to sharks.

A brief review of what we have discussed is presented in Fig. 4-5, which shows the osmotic conditions in the major groups of animals. Marine invertebrates (A) are in osmotic equilibrium with sea water, but can regulate their ionic composition. Marine elasmobranchs (B) have a low salt content, but are in osmotic equilibrium with sea water because they retain urea. Marine teleosts (C) are hypotonic and make up for lost water by drinking sea water and excreting the salts via the gills. Fresh-water invertebrates (D), although they vary considerably, are hypertonic to the

Fig. 4-5. This chart indicates the magnitude of the osmotic concentration in various groups of animals in relation to the concentration of sea water (dashed line at top).

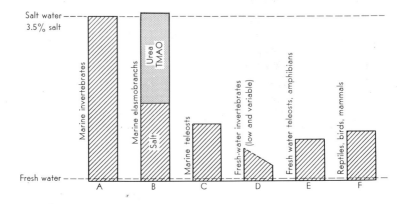

water and have mechanisms for actively absorbing salt from the very low concentration in fresh water. Fresh-water fish and amphibians (E) are in a similar situation and also absorb salt from the water. Reptiles, birds, and mammals are all terrestrial, and those that have secondarily returned to an equatic life—seals, whales, crocodiles, turtles, penguins, etc.—have retained the air-breathing habit as well as an impermeable integument. Since they are in principle still terrestrial animals, they will be discussed in the following section.

TERRESTRIAL ANIMALS

The greatest physiological threat to life on land is the danger of dehydration. This is the price terrestrial animals pay for easy access to oxygen, which permits a high metabolic rate and eventually the evolution of a warm-blooded physiology. Large-scale successful evolution of terrestrial life has taken place only in two phyla, the vertebrates and the arthropods. In addition, some snails thrive on land and are truly terrestrial, but other invertebrates that we think of as "terrestrial," e.g., sowbugs (Crustacea), earthworms (Annelida), and others, depend on a moist habitat, and if they are kept in the open air they soon succumb to desiccation.

If an animal is to maintain its normal water content, all the water it loses must be exactly replaced by water it takes up. If the total gain in water equals the loss, we say that the animal is in *water balance;* if the water loss is not covered by an equal gain, the animal is in *negative water balance,* a situation that cannot continue for long without serious effects.

Water Balance—Gain

The various avenues for water gain and loss are pictured in Fig. 4-6. Although we usually pay no attention to the first item on the "gain" side, *oxidation water,* we all know that water is formed in the combustion of

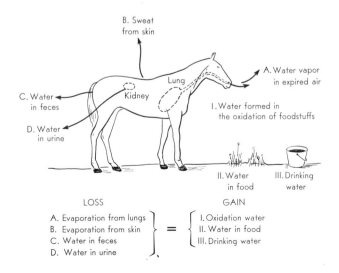

Fig. 4-6. A mammal is in water balance when all the loss of water (A, B, C, D) is equaled by the total gain in water (I, II, III).

B. Sweat from skin

A. Water vapor in expired air

C. Water in feces

Lung

Kidney

I. Water formed in the oxidation of foodstuffs

D. Water in urine

II. Water in food III. Drinking water

LOSS

A. Evaporation from lungs
B. Evaporation from skin
C. Water in feces
D. Water in urine

=

GAIN

I. Oxidation water
II. Water in food
III. Drinking water

organic materials, as is evidenced in the dew that condenses on the outside of a pot of cold water placed over a gas burner, or the water that drips out of the tail pipe of a car on a cold morning. The amount of oxidation water formed in the body depends on the particular food metabolized. Thus, when 1 gram of glucose is oxidized $(C_6H_{12}O_6 + 6\,O_2 \longrightarrow 6\,CO_2 + 6\,H_2O)$, 0.6 gram of water is formed, which is, of course, the yield whether combustion takes place in the organism or in a test tube. Because of its high content of hydrogen, one gram of fat yields 1.1 gram of water. The yield of oxidation water from protein is quite low, about 0.3 gram of H_2O per gram. In a man who does a moderate amount of light work, the metabolic rate may be 2800 kcal per day, which on an average American diet may be covered by 350 grams of carbohydrate, 100 grams of fat, and 100 grams of protein. Calculating with these figures, we find that he forms about 340 grams of oxidation water per day.

The second item on the "gain" side, *water in food,* is an important source because all food contains some free water or moisture, although the amount varies tremendously. Obviously, milk and juicy fruits contain a lot of water, but other foods also contain water, sometimes more than we would expect (see Table 4-2). Even dry breakfast cereals and crackers contain some 5–10 per cent water. Since food habits vary so much, it is difficult to estimate how much water is taken in with the food.

Table 4-2

WATER CONTENT
OF VARIOUS FOODSTUFFS

Food	Gm. water/ 100 gm. food
Lettuce	95
Strawberries	90
Carrots	88
Milk	87
Apples	84
Potatoes	78
Cottage cheese	76
Eggs	74
Fish	65–80
Meats	50–70
Cheese	40
Bread	35
Raisins	24
Butter	15
Crackers	5

The third item on our "gain" list, *drinking water,* varies the most, since it is accurately regulated to meet the needs of the individual organism. The major stimulus to drinking is "thirst," a feeling that seems quite clear to us, but physiologically is ill defined. When we lack water, the salivary secretion decreases and the mouth and throat become dry, but this dryness cannot be the only factor in thirst, for moistening the mouth does not relieve thirst. The main stimulus to drinking apparently comes from a center in the hypothalamus in the brain, which is stimulated when the osmotic concentration of the blood is increased because of water loss. It is interesting to note that eating salt food has the same effect. The actual location of the center has been established by the injection of small amounts of concentrated salt solution into various parts of the brain of goats. When the correct spot is injected, the animal drinks huge quantities of water, although its body is not at all water-depleted.

Water Balance—Loss

On a cold day when steam condenses from our breath, we can clearly see that the *expired air* contains a great deal of moisture; it is, in fact, saturated with water vapor after passing over the moist surfaces of the lungs and respiratory passages. The amount of water evaporated from the lungs of warm-blooded animals is appreciable, but is difficult to calculate exactly because the inspired air will contain some moisture, and it is only the difference between this and saturation that is added in the respiratory tract. When the ventilation of the lungs is increased with a rise in metabolism, more water is lost, and the amount corresponds to the additional air taken into the lungs to supply the need for oxygen.

An average man who does not work too heavily may take 10,000 liters of air into his lungs per day, which, when it is expired, will contain some 400 grams of water. The amount actually removed from the body will be less, depending on the humidity of the inspired air. At ordinary room temperature and 50 per cent relative humidity, the 10,000 liters of air would contain about 100 grams of water, and about 300 grams would be lost from the lungs.

As we discussed in Chapter 3, water is a crucial factor in heat regulation, but even when there is no visible sweating some water evaporates from the *skin*. In a man, this amount is about one-half liter per day. If sweating occurs, of course, evaporation increases sharply and may reach 10 to 15 liters per day.

In man, some 100 grams or more of water per day are lost in the *feces*. The relative bulk of the feces varies with the diet, and, particularly in plant eaters, the large quantities of undigested fibrous material carry a great deal of water out of the animal. In a cow, for example, the amount may be 20 to 40 liters per day.

In man, the amount of water in the *urine* is normally 1000 to 1500 grams per day, although the amount varies greatly. If the water intake is scant, the kidney eliminates the excretory products with as little water as possible; in other words, the kidney produces a very concentrated urine. In man, the minimum urine output is about 300 grams per day. If the water intake is excessive, the kidney increases the urine volume accordingly in order to maintain the normal water content of the body. The volume of the urine is controlled by a substance, antidiuretic hormone (ADH), which is released from the *hypophysis* gland at the base of the brain in response to an increased osmotic concentration in the blood. When it reaches the kidney via the blood, it causes the kidney to withhold water, thus reducing the urine volume. When the blood is more dilute, on the other hand, less ADH is released and the urine volume increases, eliminating the excess water. This mechanism for regulating urine volume combines with the accurate regulation of water intake by thirst to keep the water content of the body at just the needed level.

The kidney, aside from its function in conserving water or excreting an excess of it, plays a major role in eliminating a host of dissolved substances. Starches and fats pose no special problem of excretion, for the end products of their metabolism are only water and carbon dioxide. Protein, however, in addition to CO_2 and water, yields metabolic products that contain the nitrogen from the amino acids. Numerous other organic compounds found in food are only partly metabolized, giving products that must be eliminated. Salts must, in the long run, be excreted in the same amount as taken in, or they will accumulate in the organism. In fact, all the material that is absorbed from the intestine, unless used for growth, must leave again, and, except for CO_2 and water, the kidney excretes almost all of it. (Minor amounts, such as the break-down products of hemoglobin, are eliminated via the bile, and a small amount of material is lost from the skin, but this is generally insignificant except in the excretion of sodium chloride during heavy sweating.)

Nitrogen Excretion

In living organisms, the major nitrogen-containing substances are proteins. In animals, these are never completely metabolized to yield free nitrogen, but always result in end products that contain nitrogen in chemical combination. The commonest end products are:

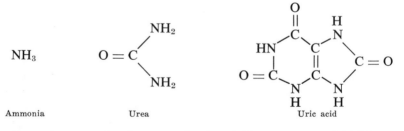

| Ammonia | Urea | Uric acid |

Ammonia, a gas that is tremendously soluble in water and highly toxic to animals, is the immediate break-down product of amino acids. In many aquatic animals, particularly in invertebrates, it is rapidly excreted to the surrounding water and thus does not build up to toxic concentrations. Terrestrial animals, not having an unlimited water supply, rapidly synthesize the ammonia into more complex and less toxic compounds and then excrete them. Mammals, amphibians, and fishes excrete *urea,* whereas *uric acid* is the end product in birds and most reptiles, insects, and terrestrial snails. Formed in the liver from the nitrogen of amino acids and then excreted by the kidney, urea is a neutral compound that is easily soluble in water and that has a relatively low toxicity. Elasmobranch fishes retain urea in order to increase the osmotic concentration of their blood to equal that of the sea water. Although teleost fishes excrete much nitrogen as ammonia, they also form some urea.

Since urea is easily soluble in water, it must be excreted in a liquid urine, which, however, drains off the much needed water reserves of terrestrial animals. The excretion of uric acid, on the other hand, since the acid is almost insoluble, has definite advantages. When urine is formed, uric acid crystallizes out from solution and water is reabsorbed, thus enabling birds and many reptiles, insects, and terrestrial snails to excrete nitrogen with the loss of very little water. The droppings from chickens and other birds have a dark brownish portion of fecal matter and a whitish mass of semi-solid urine, containing a suspension of uric acid crystals.

The formation of uric acid may be even more important in the development of the embryo than in conserving the water of the adult. All the animal groups that form uric acid from amino acids lay eggs although the birth of living young has secondarily evolved in some cases. Since the embryo must develop on the limited supply of water present in the egg, it will fare much better if excretory products are deposited as insoluble material. Ammonia would be much too toxic, and how would the embryo eliminate the liquid urine formed if urea were the end product? In mammals, whose embryos give off the excretory products to the blood of the mother, urea is the main nitrogenous excretory product. In amphibians, whose embryos develop in water, ammonia is excreted but at the time of metamorphosis the product changes to urea.

Many other compounds besides proteins contain nitrogen, although they are not quantitatively as important as proteins. Among these are the nucleic acids, which in man give rise to the uric acid that is present in a small amount in the urine. In other mammals, an enzyme transforms uric acid to allantoin; in many amphibians and fish, the allantoin is further broken down to yield urea, and in aquatic invertebrates, ammonia is frequently the end product of nucleic-acid metabolism. The situation is therefore one in which the more "primitive" animal degrades uric acid by a set of enzymes that is absent in the higher vertebrates.

The Structure of the Kidney

To understand the function of the kidney, we must know its structure in some detail. In man, each kidney contains about one million single units, called *nephrons* (Fig. 4-7). Each nephron consists of a round *Malpighian body,* which is filled with a network of blood capillaries (*glomerulus*), and a urine-carrying tube which in mammals is divided into three parts—the *proximal tubule* nearest the Malpighian body, a *thin segment,* and the *distal tubule,* which joins with other tubules to form *collecting ducts* that open into the *pelvis* of the kidney. Part of the tubule, including the thin segment, makes a hairpin loop which is called *Henle's loop.* Surrounding the entire

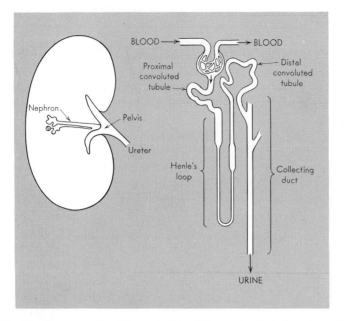

Fig. 4-7. The mammalian kidney consists of thousands of single units, nephrons, one of which is shown in the kidney at left. At right, a nephron is enlarged, showing how it begins in a capillary tuft where an initial fluid is formed by ultrafiltration. This fluid is then modified and greatly reduced in volume as it passes down the tubule and collecting duct until it reaches the ureter as urine.

tubule are blood capillaries that form hairpin loops parallel to the tubule in the region of Henle's loop. From the pelvis, the *ureter* leads to the bladder, where the urine is temporarily stored. Urine is continuously formed in the kidney and periodically discharged from the bladder.

All mammalian kidneys have essentially the same structure, although the relative length of the various parts of the tubule varies. Bird kidneys contain Malpighian bodies and looped tubules, but all cold-blooded vertebrates lack the loop structure and are unable to form a urine more concentrated than the blood, because the loop structure is essential to this process.

Formation of Urine

In the capillary loops of the Malpighian bodies, the blood pressure forces water and dissolved substances out through the capillary wall. The proteins of the plasma (and the red cells), however, do not pass through the semi-permeable capillary wall, which thus separates the small molecules that filter through from the larger ones that do not. This selective process is called *ultrafiltration,* and is similar to the passage of fluid out of the capillaries in other parts of the body (see p. 30).

Since the proteins do not pass the capillary wall, they will have the osmotic effect of trying to pull water back into the capillary. To get fluid to pass out, a pressure greater than the osmotic effect of the plasma proteins is needed. Normally, the blood pressure is about 120 mm Hg, and the osmotic pressure of the plasma proteins is about 25–30 mm Hg, but if we lower the blood pressure in the kidney by clamping the renal artery, thus gradually restricting the blood flow, all formation of fluid ceases when the pressure in the glomerulus falls to the level of the osmotic pressure of the plasma proteins. This experiment is important in proving that an ultrafiltration actually takes place. Furthermore, if we puncture the Malpighian body in a frog kidney and run a microanalysis of the minute samples of fluid formed, we will find the fluid to be a true ultrafiltrate, containing salts, sugar, amino acids, and other substances of low molecular size from the blood plasma, but no proteins.

About 130 ml of filtrate are formed per minute in the glomeruli of the two kidneys of man, but this fluid is greatly modified and reduced in volume before it reaches the ureter. A normal urine flow in man may be about 1 ml per minute—i.e., over 99 per cent of the water of the filtrate is re-absorbed as the fluid passes through the tubule and collecting ducts.

The filtrate contains a number of substances (the most vital are glucose and amino acids) that the body could not afford to lose in large quantities, and these substances are removed from the tubular fluid. The transport, which moves from a concentration in the tubule that gradually approaches zero to a higher concentration in the blood, is an active transport that is carried out by the tubular cells. This *active re-absorption* takes place in the proximal tubule, where sodium chloride also is re-absorbed. When these large amounts of solutes are removed, the concentration of the tubular fluid decreases, and water moves back to the blood because of the osmotic concentration difference. This process is called the *passive re-absorption* of water. As the fluid passes through the distal portions of the tubule, additional water is removed (see below) and other modifications take place, one of which is the *active secretion* from the blood into the tubule. One substance secreted in this way is penicillin, which is excreted very rapidly because the glomerulus filters it and additional amounts are secreted into the tubule as the fluid passes down.

FORMATION OF A CONCENTRATED URINE.   Lower vertebrates are unable to form a urine with a higher osmotic concentration than their blood plasma. Only birds and mammals can concentrate the urine above the plasma, and only these have nephrons with a characteristic loop structure. Careful studies of the kidney function of various mammals have shown that the loop is responsible for the concentrating process by acting as a counter-current multiplier system. This mechanism depends on a principle characteristically different from the counter-current exchange that works as a heat exchanger in the whale flipper (page 45), and it therefore needs further explanation.

A great number of experiments, including the analysis of fluid obtained from various parts of the nephron, suggest the following system (Fig. 4-8).

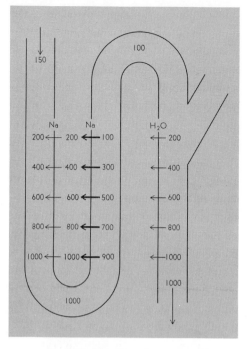

Sodium is transported actively out of
the ascending limb of Henle's loop and
accumulates in the surrounding tissue.
The walls of the ascending limb must
be impermeable to water, otherwise
water would passively follow the sodium. The walls of the collecting
ducts, on the other hand, are water-
permeable, and the high concentration
in the surrounding tissue therefore
causes an osmotic withdrawal of water
out of the collecting ducts, leading to
a concentration of the fluid in them
(urine). Actual determinations on
fluids from the various parts of the
nephron show that the glomerular
filtrate is isotonic, the fluid at the tip
of Henle's loop is highly concentrated,
but in the distal convoluted tubule it
is iso- or hypotonic, whereas in the
collecting duct it finally becomes concentrated again. Additional support
for this sequence of events is found in
the observation that not only the fluid
in the loop but also the entire surrounding tissue has a high osmotic
concentration which increases towards
the tip of the papilla, and that the
fluid in the collecting duct attains a
final osmotic concentration similar to
that of the tissue around it.

The way the counter-current multiplier works to build up an increasing
concentration is as follows: As sodium is actively transported out of the
ascending limb and the concentration in the surrounding tissues is increased,
some of it diffuses into the descending limb. This means that the fluid that
now reaches the ascending limb has a higher-than-before concentration of
sodium, and more can be transported out and diffuse into the descending
limb. What actually happens is that sodium is constantly being removed
from the ascending limb and returned to the descending one, thus causing
an accumulation of sodium in the loop. The characteristic feature of a
counter-current multiplier system is that it permits the attainment of very
high concentrations, although the transport process as such does not necessarily have the capacity to establish as great concentration differences. The
diagram in Fig. 4-8 shows that the cells of the ascending limb in no place

transport sodium over a gradient of more than 100 mN. From one end of the loop to the other, however, the concentration difference in the diagram is 850 mN. This arrangement has the advantage that a relatively modest transport system can be multiplied into a concentration difference many times as high as the maximum capacity of the transporting cells. Furthermore, no single tubular cell is exposed to a concentration difference as great as that between the blood plasma (150 mN) and the final urine (1000 mN).

It should be noted that a counter-current multiplier system is completely dependent on two prerequisites: There must be an active, energy-requiring transport, and there must be a hairpin-loop structure for the multiplying effect to occur.

THE ACTION OF ANTIDIURETIC HORMONE. The volume of urine produced is controlled by the antidiuretic hormone (ADH), which is released from the hypophysis. Under the influence of ADH more water is reabsorbed, the urine volume goes down and its concentration up; in the absence of ADH urine volume goes up and concentration down. ADH acts by increasing the permeability to water of the collecting ducts so that more water diffuses out and leaves a more concentrated urine in the duct.

WATER BALANCE IN EXTREME ENVIRONMENTS

Rats That Never Drink

Drinking water is not always easily available to animals, especially in deserts where years may elapse between rainfalls. Nevertheless, the deserts of the world abound with animals that can survive without drinking, and among these are the kangaroo rats (*Dipodomys*). Despite their name, kangaroo rats are rodents and not marsupials. They live on seeds and other dry plant material, and eat little or no green and succulent food. In the laboratory, they have been kept for months on a diet of only barley or rolled oats, although they will nibble on lettuce if it is given to them. How can these animals get along seemingly without water?

To begin with, the bodies of kangaroo rats contain as much water as those of other mammals (an average of 66 per cent). Even when they have eaten only dry food for weeks or months, the water content remains the same, indicating that they keep their body water and maintain their water balance on the dry food, i.e., the water loss does not exceed the gain. The water gain is easily analyzed: For every 100 grams of barley consumed, 54 grams of oxidation water are formed, and, in addition, a small percentage of water is absorbed in the grain. Since the kangaroo rat takes about a month to eat 100 grams of barley, it must economize to the utmost to keep its meager water supply in balance. The animals have no sweat glands and do not need water for heat regulation because they are nocturnal and search for food only during the cool nights. Evaporation from the lungs is inevitable, however, and is the greatest single source of water expenditure in the kangaroo rat. The feces, on the other hand, have a very low water content and take only a small fraction of the available water.

The most remarkable physiological characteristic of the kangaroo rat is its capacity to eliminate excretory products in a small volume of very concentrated urine. Its kidney has a concentrating ability that far exceeds that of other mammals (see Table 4-3), and it therefore wastes much less

Table 4-3

MAXIMUM CONCENTRATIONS OF SALT AND UREA IN URINE

Animal	Salt	Urea
Man	0.37 N (2.2%)	1.0 M (6%)
White rat	0.60 N (3.5%)	2.5 M (15%)
Kangaroo rat	1.2 N (7.0%)	3.8 M (23%)

water in urine formation. Since it can excrete salt in a concentration twice that in sea water, we would expect it to be able to drink sea water with impunity. If it is fed soy beans, a kangaroo rat will be driven to drink, because the high protein content of the beans causes such large amounts of urea to be formed that extra water is required to excrete it. Under these circumstances, the kangaroo rat will even drink sea water, which would poison man or other animals but does not harm him because his kidney is powerful enough to excrete the salts.

The Camel and the Desert Heat

The camel's legendary ability to abstain from water and march for days in the desert, eating only thorny bushes, has been so widely advertised that even scientists have trouble separating fact from fable. What is the actual situation?

Since the camel cannot, like the kangaroo rat, avoid the scorching heat of the desert day by hiding in an underground burrow, it must employ water for temperature regulation. Does it store a water supply? Travelers have reported that an Arab who is trapped without water in the desert sometimes saves his life by killing his camel and drinking the water he finds in its stomach. The camel's rumen does contain a great deal of fluid mixed with the fermenting food, just as do the rumens of other ruminants, and since this fluid has the same osmotic concentration as the blood, it could be drunk in an emergency. The belief that the rumen fluid is stored water has been given credulity by the peculiar anatomy of the camel's rumen, which is lined with pocket-like structures. These have erroneously been called "water sacks," but they are anatomically unsuited to water storage and actually contain food being digested.

Contrary to popular notion, no water is stored in the hump. It is almost pure fat, and when this fat is metabolized the usual amount of oxidation water is formed. This water, however, does not constitute a net gain to the body, for the oxygen required for the oxidation increases the ventilation of the lungs and thus causes the water loss to exceed the amount formed by oxidation.

The camel, then, does not store water, and must carefully conserve what it takes up. For animals exposed to desert heat, the water used to cool their bodies is irretrievably lost. Could the amount thus lost somehow be reduced? A man in the desert keeps his body temperature at about 37°C by sweating, but the camel lets his temperature climb to about 41°C before he sweats enough to prevent a further rise; furthermore, in the early morning the camel's temperature may be as low as 34°C, which gives him the advantage of a low starting point to face the heat of the day. During the day, then, he can allow his body temperature to rise gradually to its maximum level, without expending a large quantity of water in trying to keep it down. The camel's fur also helps ward off the environmental heat, for a well-insulated body gains heat only gradually, just as a block of ice melts more slowly when wrapped in cloths. The fur must not be too thick, of course, because it must allow water to be evaporated from the skin surface in order to dissipate the heat produced in metabolism.

In addition to being an efficient conserver of water, the camel has an unusual tolerance to dehydration of the body. If most mammals lose as much as 20 per cent of their body water, they die, but the camel can lose over 40 per cent without serious danger. This tolerance, combined with their slow rate of water loss, enables camels to go without water for much longer periods than other mammals, and when they do fill up again, they drink great quantities to make up for the loss. Some have been seen to drink close to one-third their body weight in ten minutes.

Do Whales Drink Sea Water?

What of whales—and seals, too—who never have access to fresh water? Most whales and seals solve their problem by eating fish, which have a high water content and an osmotic concentration of about one-third that of sea water, i.e., a low salt content. Fish, however, have a high protein content, which necessitates the formation of much urea that must then be excreted in the urine. In the end, though, whales and seals, whose kidneys can excrete a rather concentrated urine, gain more water from the fish than they lose through the urine or in evaporation from the lungs, and thus they do not have to drink at all.

A man adrift in the sea does not fare so well. If he drinks sea water, which contains 3.5 per cent salt, he will expend extra water removing the salt from his body, since his kidneys can at best produce a urine with only 2.2 per cent salt (see Table 4-3), and he thereby increases the dehydration of his body and hastens his death. He would not be much better off eating raw fish, for in spite of the fish's relatively low salt content, the protein in fish would form urea that would require water for excretion. Man's kidneys, in short, are not efficient enough to enable him to live like the seals and whales.

The sea mammals that eat invertebrate organisms take in more salt than do those that eat fish, for invertebrates are in osmotic equilibrium with sea water. The baleen whales feed on planktonic crustaceans, and the walrus eats mussels and clams that it tears loose from the bottom of the ocean with its long tusks. How do they manage? Although the water balance of these animals has not been studied, urine samples from whales show that their kidney can elaborate a urine more concentrated than sea water and thus excrete the excess salt contained in their invertebrate diet or in sea water incidentally swallowed during feeding.

Being mammals, seals and whales lose additional water when they suckle their young. They produce a very concentrated milk containing 30 to 40 per cent fat, compared to the 4 per cent fat usually contained in cow's milk. This high percentage of fat probably does not serve primarily to facilitate the rapid growth of the young, for the offspring of many mammals with a dilute milk grow quickly, but to economize on the mother's water.

Fig. 4-9. Marine birds are able to drink sea water because a special gland, the salt gland, can eliminate the salt that the kidney cannot handle. In the herring gull, the glands are two flat, crescent-shaped organs on top of the skull above the eyes. (From K. Schmidt-Nielsen, Scientific American, 200, January, 1959.)

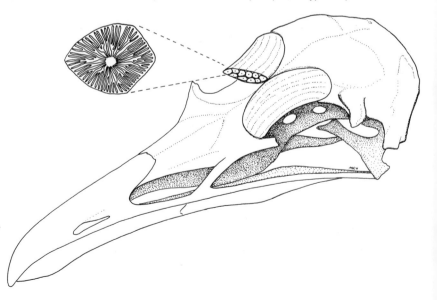

A Dripping Nose and Turtle Tears

Many birds live at sea, sometimes hundreds of miles from land and fresh water. Do they drink sea water? As we have seen, the prerequisite for a marine life in mammals is a powerful kidney that can excrete high salt concentrations, but the bird kidney has not evolved to the efficiency of the mammalian kidney. Birds do have the advantage of excreting uric acid, which requires much less water than urea, but this does not help the salt situation.

All marine birds—gulls, albatrosses, penguins, and so on—however, have a gland in the head that can excrete a highly concentrated solution of sodium chloride (Fig. 4-9). This gland, which has a structure entirely different from the kidney, can excrete a salt solution up to twice the concentration of sea water. When the birds ingest food with a high salt content or drink sea water, the gland secretes the excess salt; the secretion flows through the salt-gland ducts into the nasal cavity and drips off from the tip of the beak. The salt gland secretes only sodium chloride and none of the many other substances excreted by the kidney, and it functions only when there is a salt load; otherwise it is at rest. In contrast, the kidney produces urine continuously.

Marine reptiles have salt problems similar to those of marine birds, but their kidney is even less efficient in its concentrating ability. The large sea turtles have a salt gland close to the eye, and the duct opens in the corner of the eye. This gland functions like the salt gland of the birds, and explains the well-known fact that sea turtles cry tears when they go ashore to lay their eggs in sandy beaches.

Movements

CHAPTER FIVE

Most animals, in contrast to plants and microbes, are free to swim, crawl, run, or fly. When a man moves, his skeleton functions as a system of rigid but articulated levers that are moved by the muscles. The same principle is involved whether the skeleton consists of rods immersed in muscle, as in vertebrates, or of tubes surrounding the muscle, as in crabs or insects. In either case, the force of muscle contraction is transmitted to a mechanical system, resulting in organized movement of legs, wings, fins, and so on.

Most multicellular animals have muscles, even though they may lack a skeleton. In the earthworm, for example, the body wall consists of two sets of muscles, one longitudinal, running lengthwise along the body, and the other circular around the body. If the circular muscles contract and the longitudinal ones relax, the blood (coelomic fluid) transmits the pressure so that the body becomes longer and thinner. When the earthworm moves, the front end is first pushed out in this way, and then the hind end moves up as the longitudinal muscles contract and shorten the body. Fine bristles along the body prevent the worm from sliding back.

68

The leech has a similar system of muscular body walls; it extends its front end and attaches the front sucker, pulls its hind end up, and, after attaching the hind sucker, stretches out again. The more primitive animals, including all the unicellular ones, lack muscles, but some can nevertheless move about. How they manage to do so will be further discussed toward the end of this chapter.

The muscles responsible for the movements of larger animals consist of numerous fibers that are supplied with nerves. When nerve impulses reach the fibers, the fibers shorten or contract with considerable force, and when the nerve impulses cease, the muscle becomes limp again and can be stretched without resistance.

THE PHYSIOLOGY OF MUSCLE

Vertebrate Skeletal Muscle

RECORDING OF MUSCLE CONTRACTIONS. If a frog is killed and one of its muscles is removed, this muscle can continue to work and contract for several hours. Such isolated muscles can tell us a great deal because we can control the conditions affecting them and can easily measure their contractions. Muscles from warm-blooded animals could also be used, but they are more sensitive: They must be kept warm and supplied with oxygen, or even better, with blood. Even then, they deteriorate much faster than do the muscles of cold-blooded animals. If we select relatively thin frog muscles, oxygen can diffuse into the muscle and enable it to continue work while drawing on its energy reserves. A typical experiment used to record the contraction of a muscle is shown in Fig. 5-1. Although the arrangement is simple, much can be learned about muscle from it.

The cells of muscle and nerve, like other cells, respond to electricity. When we apply an electric current, we find that the first response follows immediately after the current begins to flow, but that continuing the current has no further effect. When we stop the current, we see another response. Thus it is a *change* in current, whether up or down, that stimulates. If the current is extremely weak, we see no response, but if it exceeds a certain value—the *threshold value,* or *rheobase*—the nerve responds by propagating a normal impulse and the muscle responds by contracting. Thus, the electric current, whether applied to the nerve or directly to the muscle, will trigger a contraction.

Figure 5-2A is the record of a muscular contraction produced by a single short electric pulse. After the stimulus is applied, a short period, called the *latent period,* elapses before contraction starts. In a frog the latent period lasts about 0.01 second, and the combined contraction and relaxation last about 0.1 second. If a stimulus is applied to the nerve instead of directly to the muscle, the response will be delayed while the impulse travels through the nerve. By moving the stimulating electrodes

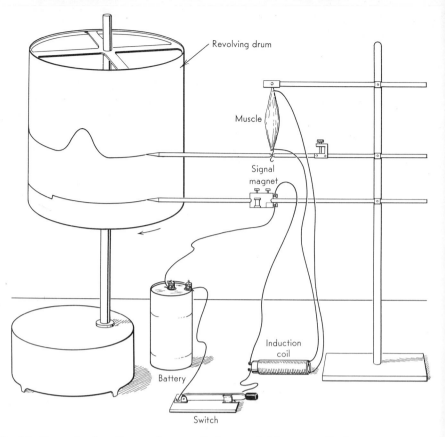

Fig. 5-1. The contraction of a muscle can easily be recorded by means of a lever that writes on a revolving drum covered with paper. The lower lever in the drawing is attached to a signal magnet, which records when the electric circuit is closed in the primary circuit of the induction coil. In this case, when the switch was closed, the induction coil sent a single pulse of induced current from the secondary coil through the muscle. The duration of the contraction is indicated by the spread of the curve, and can be calculated if we know how fast the drum moves.

Fig. 5-2. Records of the tension in a leg muscle of a cat when prevented from shortening (isometric contraction). A single electric pulse (lower line) gives the typical curve for a single muscle contraction (A). A short period, the latent period, elapses before contraction starts. A second stimulus gives a second contraction which is superimposed on the first (B and C).

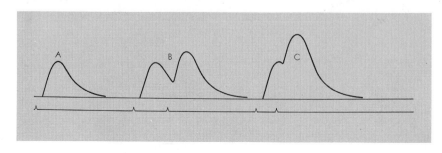

to a more distant point on the nerve and measuring the increase in time, we can find how fast the impulse passes through the nerve. With exactly this set-up, Helmholtz in 1850 was able to measure the *rate of conduction* in a frog nerve, which is about 25 m/sec.

If we apply a second stimulus before the first contraction is ended, a new contraction is superimposed on the first (Fig. 5-2B and C). If we continue applying closely spaced stimuli, we get a smooth, sustained contraction, called a *tetanus* (Fig. 5-3A and B). All normal contractions in the skeletal muscles of vertebrates are tetanic, i.e., responses to volleys of impulses in the nerves; single twitches probably never occur.

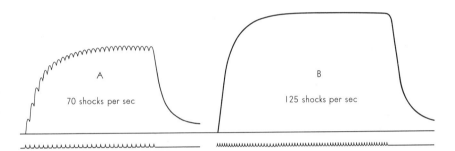

A
70 shocks per sec

B
125 shocks per sec

Fig. 5-3. Tension in the eye-muscle of a cat when stimulated by a series of electric impulses (the scales are different from those in the previous figure). Repeated stimuli give a prolonged contraction (A), which, if the impulses are sufficiently frequent, fuses to a completely smooth sustained contraction, called a tetanus (B).

ELECTRICAL EVENTS DURING MUSCLE CONTRACTION. A muscle consists of a very large number of single fibers, each with a diameter between 0.01 and 0.1 mm. In a resting muscle fiber, a difference in electric potential always exists between the outer surface and the inside of the fiber. The outside is positive relative to the inside, and the potential difference is about 90 to 100 mV.* The potential is due to the differences in ion concentrations inside and outside. There is a selective transport of sodium ions out of the fiber, and this causes a redistribution of potassium and chloride with an excess of positive ions on the surface (Fig. 5-4).† We do not know the actual nature of the transport mechanism, but since it works against the concentration gradient, it is an active transport and is commonly referred to as the "sodium pump."

The moment a nerve impulse arrives at the muscle fiber, the membrane potential is momentarily abolished, or even slightly reversed, and the fiber contracts. For a brief moment, the fiber behaves as if it permits

* One millivolt (mV) equals one-thousandth of a volt.
† The potential difference across the membrane is actually due to the Gibbs-Donnan equilibrium for potassium.

the extruded sodium ions to diffuse in, thus eliminating the potential difference and depolarizing the membrane. The membrane potential, however, is immediately restored, and the muscle fiber is able to react anew. The membrane can be depolarized in various ways—by mechanical stimulation, by a change in pH, by the application of certain chemicals, etc.—but the normal cause is the arrival of a nerve impulse, to be discussed in Chapter 7. Depolarization of the muscle membrane is always followed by contraction, but it is not known how this happens.

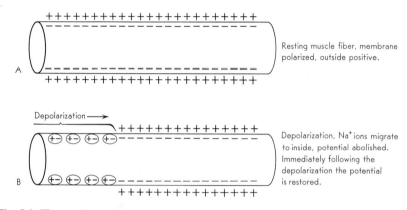

Fig. 5-4. The outside surface of a muscle fiber is positively charged when the fiber is at rest (A). When a nerve impulse arrives, the surface potential is momentarily abolished (B), and the fiber contracts. As reconstitution proceeds the sodium ions are actively transported out of the fiber.

THE ALL-OR-NONE RESPONSE. In vertebrate muscle, the degree of contraction in a *single fiber* does not depend on the strength of the stimulus. Below the rheobase there is no response, but if the stimulus exceeds the rheobase, the fiber contracts at its maximum, and a further increase in the strength of stimulus causes no further increase in contraction. By changing the temperature or slightly stretching the fiber before the contraction occurs, we can vary the force of contraction, but we cannot alter it by changing the strength of the stimulus; either the fiber does not respond at all or it responds to the full extent. In physiology, this type of reaction is called an *all-or-none response*.

How can muscles contract with varying force when the single fibers have an all-or-none response? The nerve leading to the muscle contains a large number of single nerve fibers; each splits up into branches which reach several muscle fibers. The unit of one nerve fiber and its many connected muscle fibers is called a *motor unit*. In small, accurately-controlled muscles such as the eye muscle, one motor unit may have less than 10 muscle fibers, but in the major skeletal muscles the number may be several hundred. This arrangement has the advantage that in a large muscle the number of fibers in the nerve can be kept to a reasonable level. The seemingly infinite gradation in the strength with which a whole muscle can contract depends on how many fibers in the nerve carry impulses, in other words, on how many of the motor units are stimulated. If a muscle is active for a period of time, the motor units work in relays so that some rest while others are active.

Invertebrate Muscle

After we have learned the simple rules of the all-or-none response in vertebrate muscle, we are in for some surprises when we turn to the invertebrates. In a sea anemone, for example, a single impulse in a nerve produces no muscular response, but a second impulse will cause a contraction, and the shorter the interval between the two impulses the more powerful the contraction. Although the first impulse failed to cause a contraction, it must have produced some effect that made it possible for the second impulse to get through. This effect is called *facilitation,* an important concept in muscle and nerve physiology.

Many invertebrate muscles, particularly in crustaceans, are supplied with two or more nerves. In such muscles the single muscle fiber is connected with two types of nerve fiber, one excitatory and the other inhibitory. If the inhibitory fiber is stimulated, impulses in the excitatory fiber will not cause contraction. In the claw of the crab, the innervation is such that when the closing muscle is stimulated, the opening muscle is at the same time inhibited, and vice versa. The claw muscles frequently have one set of inhibitory and two sets of stimulating fibers. Impulses in one set of stimulating fibers cause a quick contraction, and in the other a slower, more prolonged and forceful contraction. Since the same muscle fiber responds differently to the impulses in the two fibers, the difference must be in the nerves, but how this comes about is unknown. Still, the more we learn about invertebrate muscle, the clearer it becomes that the all-or-none response of the vertebrate muscle is a special case and not the general rule, and that multiple innervation is a common way of controlling contraction.

Insect Flight Muscles

Some insect movements are so fast that they could not possibly be produced by tetanic contractions, or even by a single twitch. The minimum time required for a complete cycle of contraction and relaxation of a muscle receiving a single nerve impulse appears to be about 15 to 20 msec.* At this rate, only about 50, or at the most 70, complete cycles

* One millisecond (msec) is one-thousandth of a second.

could occur in one second. The wing beat in some insects, however, is much faster than this—in mosquitoes it may be several hundred per second—and the muscles must work this rapidly. But the flight muscles receive nerve impulses at a frequency much lower than the rate of wing beat; e.g., there may be only 1 impulse for each 3 or 4 wing movements.

The explanation for this unusual phenomenon lies in the fact that the wings, wing muscles, and thorax form an elastic system that can be brought into resonant oscillating vibrations, and the timing of the nerve impulses is such that these reinforce the oscillations. As the system vibrates, the muscles are stretched with each oscillation, and they respond to stretching by a contraction; thus the contractions will always occur at the resonant frequency of the entire system. If the wings are loaded with small weights or are cut off, we should expect that the change in mass would cause the system to oscillate at a different frequency, and this is exactly what happens. Not all flying insects have flight muscles that receive nerve stimulation at a lower frequency than the frequency of contraction; many slow fliers have a 1:1 ratio between nerve impulses and muscle contractions.

Cardiac Muscle

The vertebrate heart is a hollow muscle that forces out the blood as it contracts. Its structure is different from that of skeletal muscle, which is made up of parallel muscle fibers, arranged in bundles. The fibers of the heart form a more irregular meshwork. The connections between adjoining fibers are numerous and intimate, and when a contraction starts at the sinus node it spreads to all fibers throughout the entire heart. Since the individual fiber follows the all-or-none rule, the whole heart does the same; that is, once a contraction starts, it continues until maximum contraction is reached. When the muscle fibers are stretched, which happens if the heart is filled with additional blood before contraction begins, the force of contraction is increased (the contraction is still an all-or-none effect).

That the force of contraction is strengthened with increased stretching (up to a certain limit) enables the heart automatically to adjust its work output. Suppose there is a sudden increase in resistance in the peripheral circulation. Immediately, at the next contraction, the heart is prevented from pumping out the usual amount of blood. At the onset of the following heart beat, more blood than usual remains in the ventricle and the fibers are stretched, causing the contraction to be more forceful. This in turn raises the arterial pressure to compensate for the increased resistance. Contrarily, the heart automatically adjusts to expel the blood with less force if it meets less resistance. The heart muscle's ability to regulate the strength of its contraction is one of several mechanisms that allow the heart to function effectively as a variable pump.

Smooth Muscle

The muscles of internal organs of vertebrates have features that are different from those in skeletal muscle, the most apparent difference being that the fibers lack the microscopic cross-striations that can be seen in skeletal and heart muscle. The smooth muscles most commonly studied by physiologists are those in the intestine, stomach, bladder, uterus, and arteries. In these organs the muscle fibers are short and are packed in layers rather than in discrete bundles.

Although researchers have studied cut-out strips of smooth muscle intensively, these muscles are not as well understood as skeletal muscle. It is even difficult to define accurately the differences between the two types, but some major ones are apparent. The smooth muscle, for example, *contracts more slowly* than skeletal muscle, and most smooth muscles may contract *spontaneously*. Smooth muscle has *no definite resting length;* the length may change without a change in the force applied to the muscle. On the other hand, smooth muscle *responds to stretching* by immediate contraction. In the body, smooth muscle maintains a certain slight tension, called *tonus,* that has the nature of a prolonged contraction not followed by a relaxation phase. Thus, the muscular walls of intestine, bladder, blood vessels, etc., have a certain tonus or tone which exerts a continuous force or pressure against the contents. Smooth muscle is controlled by a double set of nerves, the sympathetic and parasympathetic nerves, which, in an antagonistic manner, modify the muscle's spontaneous activity by liberating adrenalin and acetylcholine, respectively; these substances seem to act directly on the smooth muscle cells.

In invertebrates as well as in vertebrates, striated muscle generally produces fast movements, and smooth, unstriated muscle slow movements, but the distinction is not clear. In insects, for example, all muscles, even those of the intestine, seem to be striated. An interesting case of separation into fast, striated fibers and slow, smooth fibers occurs in the scallop (*Pecten*), which, although a mussel, can swim by flapping its shells. Most mussels have one or two closing muscles that hold the shells firmly together, and these muscles have a very slow rate of relaxation, i.e., they work as if the single muscle twitch pictured in Fig. 5-2 were drawn out in time, so that the period during which near-maximum force is exerted would last much longer. In Pecten, however, the closing muscle has two components, a fast, striated portion for swimming and a slow, smooth portion for keeping the shells closed.

Modified Muscle—Electric Fish

That some fish can give electric shocks has been known for centuries. Even the ancient Greeks were familiar with such fish, but, being unaware of the nature of electricity, they were, of course, greatly mystified by the shocks delivered by the electric ray (*Torpedo*) and the electric catfish (*Malapterurus*). Electric fishes are the only animals that can generate strong electric discharges, and there are not many species of them. Interestingly enough, the few species of electric fish are not closely related: Some are fresh-water and some are marine species, some are teleosts and some are elasmobranchs. The most powerful shock emanates from the South American electric eel (*Electrophorus*); its discharges have been measured at 550 volts, a shock strong enough to kill other fish and perhaps even a man.

Such strong discharges are both offensive and defensive weapons. If kept in an aquarium, the electric eel will stun small fish placed in the water and then eat them at leisure. Some electric fish have such weak discharges, however, that they cannot possibly be used as a weapon. Only recently has it been found that these discharges are employed to locate prey. Electric fish are extremely sensitive to influences that affect an electric field: They can distinguish between conductors and nonconductors present in the water and can detect the presence of a stationary magnet, and these abilities supposedly help them locate other fish.

The electric organs are usually fairly large masses located in the musculature on both sides of the body or tail. They are developed from modified muscle tissue, except in the electric catfish, where they may have originated from glandular tissue. All electric organs consist of a large number of regularly arranged disc-like cells, called electroplates. The two sides of the electroplates are different, and only one side is sup-

Fig. 5-5. The electric organs of fish consist of numerous electroplates. This diagram shows only two electroplates in series, to the left when resting and to the right when discharging. In rest, the charges on the two faces of each electroplate are equal and opposed, and thus show no external potential. When the charge on one face of the plate is reversed, the potentials add up as in a group of batteries connected in series. (From R. D. Keynes and H. Martins-Ferreira, Journal of Physiology, 119, 1953.)

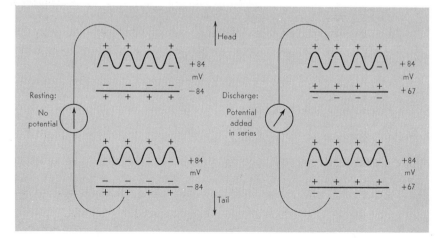

plied by a nerve. All the electroplates face in the same direction and thus produce an additive effect that is capable of building up high voltages. The electric charge in the electroplate is similar to the surface potential in a muscle fiber, where the outside is always positive relative to the inside. During the discharge, the charge is reversed on the face that receives the nerve, and the entire organ now consists of a large number of electric "batteries" arranged in series (Fig. 5-5). Such single discharges are repeated in volleys with a frequency up to several hundred single pulses per second. Acetylcholine is present in the electric organ and seems to have a role similar to that in the nervous end-plate in muscle. This fact supports the view that the physiology of the electric organ is similar to that of muscle, although the effect is so very different. An intriguing question still confronts physiologists: Why is the nervous system of an electric fish insensitive to its own powerful discharges?

MOVEMENT WITHOUT MUSCLE

Muscle is a tissue found only in multicellular animals. Many microorganisms, animals as well as plants, and also some small multicellular organisms such as flatworms (Planaria), must move by other types of locomotion, of which *ciliary* and *ameboid* movement are the most important.

CILIARY MOVEMENT. The Paramecium pictured on p. 2 belongs to a group of protozoans called ciliates. The surface of these animals is covered by thousands of small hair-like structures called *cilia,* which constantly sweep back and forth, in one direction like a stiff rod and in the backstroke much like a whiplash (Fig. 5-6). Since the cilia work in relays, their motion looks like breeze-blown waves in a field of grain. The stiff, rod-like beats are directed toward the hind end of the animal and thus propel the animal forward, while the soft, whip-like motion of the backstroke returns the cilium to the initial position with a minimum of resistance.

Since the cilia move rapidly, up to twenty beats or more per second, it is impossible to see and follow the movements of the single cilium, but we can analyze the motion in detail by taking high-speed movies through the microscope and projecting the film at slow speed. Some protozoans (flagellates) have only one or a few whip-like outgrowths, which are

Fig. 5-6. Each single cilium on the surface of a ciliated cell beats in one direction like a stiff rod (solid lines), while the backstroke (dashed lines) is accomplished with a soft whip-like motion that has much less resistance.

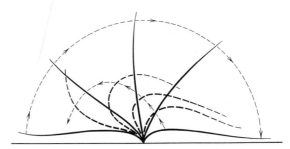

called *flagella* (Latin for whip); the spermatozoa of most animals move with flagella. Although ciliary and flagellar movement appear to be rather different, physiologically they are very similar.

Cilia can propel only very small animals. Larger animals, with their greater bulk, cannot be moved by the force of cilia only a few hundredths of a millimeter long. Many aquatic animals—sponges and mussels, for instance—use cilia to maintain currents of water for carrying oxygen, food, excretory products, etc. Ciliated cells are found in all animal phyla except Arthropoda.

AMEBOID MOVEMENT. This type of movement is exemplified by the unicellular ameba, which is a very small animal, barely visible to the unaided eye. If we observe an ameba moving, we will see that it bulges out in blunt, irregular extensions (*pseudopodia*) in the direction in which it is moving (see Fig. 1-1). As the pseudopodia attach themselves to the surface at hand, the main body of the cell begins to stream in this direction, filling and extending the size of the pseudopodium. Finally, the pseudopodium contains most of the cell and is no more a pseudopodium, but in the meantime other pesudopodia have formed. In this way, the entire cell moves slowly over the substratum at a speed of, at most, a few centimeters per hour.

Curiously, ameboid as well as ciliary movement has been retained by some cells in most of the higher animal phyla, and in man, for example, we find both ameboid and ciliated cells. The white blood cells, which can move around independently and even penetrate through the capillary wall and thus leave the blood stream, both behave and look much like amebas. The cells that line the trachea and bronchii have on their surfaces numerous cilia, which beat constantly in the direction away from the lungs and thereby slowly propel over their surface mucus and dust particles that come to lodge in the respiratory passages.

We have now seen a variety of ways in which animals travel, although we have not had time to explore the fascinating mechanics involved in swimming, running, and flying. The wheel, the most ingenious structure man has designed for the transfer of force, has never been used for propulsion by animals. This is evidently because a wheel has no direct structural connection with its shaft, and all permanent parts of the animal body require a connection to carry blood supply, nerves, etc. The more "modern" device of jet propulsion, however, appears several times in the animal kingdom. The octopus, by suddenly ejecting squirts of water from its mantle cavity, can dart backwards through the water. Similarly, the scallop, a large, heavy mussel, can rapidly flip its two shells and squirt water out between them, enabling it to leave the bottom and jerkily swim through the water.

Information

CHAPTER SIX

In order to find food, mates, and dwellings and to avoid predators and other hazards, animals need information about their surroundings. This information is gained through the sense organs or receptors, which are sensitive to a number of outside influences. The *contact receptors* give information about events at the surface of the animal, i.e. about heat, cold, pressure, touch, and chemicals (taste). Those that tell about the environment at a distance are called *distance receptors;* these are sensitive to light (vision), sound (hearing), and certain chemical substances (smell). Although distance receptors give information about conditions away from the organism, the energy or chemical in question must reach the organism and the appropriate sense organ in order to be perceived, so there is no sharp division between distance and contact receptors. Information about one's own body is given by the *proprioceptors* (*proprius* means one's own). Man usually is much less conscious of this kind of sensation than of the external senses, but he is aware at least of the position of his limbs and the position of his body in the field of gravity (he knows up from down). Pain is a sensation that may arise from the stimulation of special pain receptors, for example, in the skin, and apparently also from the stimulation of free nerve endings, for instance, in internal organs where special pain receptors are absent.

DISTANCE RECEPTORS

Light and Vision

With the aid of our eyes, we obtain a remarkable amount of information about the world around us, nearby as well as distant. What we call light is a narrow range of electromagnetic waves, with wavelengths between 380 and 760 millimicrons,* to which our eyes are sensitive. The vision of some animals extends into wavelengths slightly beyond those man can see; bees, for example, can see in the near ultraviolet range. Also within the range of animal vision is the light that produces photosynthesis in plants and the light toward which plants tend to turn in their growth. That all these very different phenomena depend on the same range of wavelengths may seem surprising, until we realize that they are all photochemical processes. The shorter wavelengths—ultraviolet, X-rays, and gamma rays—have such a high energy level that they are destructive to large, complex organic molecules, and the longer wavelengths—the infrared and the whole range of radio waves—have energy levels too low to produce extensive chemical effects.

Even animals without eyes can be sensitive to light, and they may react to light by moving toward or away from it. The earthworm, for example, remains in its burrow because it avoids light; if, at night, we shine a flashlight on one crawling halfway out of its burrow, it will withdraw instantly. Most animals that lack eyes are like the earthworm in that they can make simple responses to change in light. Our eyes, on the other hand, give much more information about our surroundings because their structure causes the formation of an image on the retina. Although the physical and chemical events occur in the eye, we displace our perception out to the place where light originated and thus perceive distant objects. Eyes that can form definite images are found in only a few of the dozen or so different animal phyla: in some molluscs (mainly octopus and squid), in a few worms, in vertebrates, and in most arthropods (crabs, spiders, and insects). The three first-mentioned phyla have eyes that are similar in structure to a photographic camera, which uses a lens to form an actual picture (Fig. 6-1). Most arthropod eyes are built on an entirely different principle; a large number of single tube-shaped *ommatidia* are arranged over a spherical surface in such a way that a composite picture can be formed, although each ommatidium forms

* One micron (μ) is one-thousandth of a millimeter, and a millimicron (mμ), consequently, is one-millionth of a millimeter.

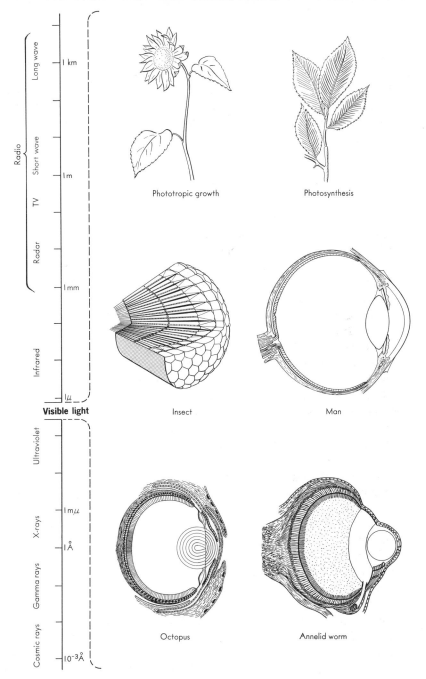

Fig. 6-1. Electromagnetic waves form a continuous band from the short cosmic rays to long radio waves. Our eyes are sensitive to only a small part of this wide range, the part which we call light. Not only are the eyes of other animals adjusted to a similar range, but even plants respond to the same wavelengths. Note that each division line on the bar stands for a tenfold increase in wavelength, going from bottom to top. The energy carried by each quantum of electromagnetic oscillation decreases tenfold for each tenfold increase in wavelength. Hence, the very energy-rich short wavelengths are destructive to organic material and the very long ones carry too little energy to have appreciable biological effects.

81

no picture but only focuses the light from a single small spot in the environment. The more ommatidia, the more precise is the composite picture, and predatory insects with good vision (e.g., dragonflies) have the largest number of ommatidia.

The different types of eyes we have mentioned have evolved independently, and there is no anatomical, embryological, or evolutionary connection between them, although the chemical processes that transmit light into nerve impulses are remarkably similar in all eyes. Eyes contain photosensitive pigments that consist of a protein to which is attached a modified molecule of vitamin A. Vitamin A has the structure of half a molecule of β-carotene, a plant pigment; it cannot be synthesized by animals and must be present in the food or be made from plant carotene. In plants, carotenes seem to be responsible for the growth response to light, and they also act as energy-transfer substances in photosynthesis by absorbing light in wavelengths where chlorophyll itself has no absorption. The carotenes, therefore, are tremendously important in the biological world; in plants they are almost universally present, and their photochemical sensitivity has been utilized in animal vision.

Color vision is extremely puzzling to the physiologist; we have no satisfactory theory of color vision, nor can we explain how we see color. For example, we cannot explain why we see white light if we mix spectrally pure red (656 mμ) and blue-green (492 mμ), or why the sensation of spectral green can be perfectly matched by a mixture of yellow and blue. We do know, however, that all shades of color can be matched by appropriate mixtures of three so-called primary colors: red, yellow, and blue. A deviating color vision, known as color blindness, is associated with reduced acuity for shades of green or red (or both). It is quite common in man, occurring in about 8 per cent of all males and 0.6 per cent of females.

From our own experience, each of us knows that he sees colors and that these colors have names, and by inference we assume (although we have no proof) that when somebody says "red" he has the same experience we have. Such inference, however, is completely unjustified when it comes to animals of a different species, with whom we cannot talk; but even so, we can discover some facts about color vision in animals. We really want the answers to two questions: first, whether an animal can see light of a given color at all and, secondly, whether different colors are perceived differently so that they can be distinguished.

Some simple tests can often answer our first question. If a chicken is fed in a dark room that has rice grains scattered on the floor and the grains are illuminated with pure spectral colors, the animals will pick up all the grains in red, yellow, and green light, but not the ones in blue light, although these are clearly visible to us. Evidently, the chicken eye is not able to perceive blue as light. In a similar fashion, we can show that honeybees are insensitive to red, and, by using red light, we can observe their life in the "darkness" inside the hive without disturbing them. On the other hand, bees are sensitive to ultraviolet, which we do not see.

Our second question—can animals distinguish colors?—has been answered by training experiments. If, for example, bees are trained to feed from a dish of sugar solution placed on a yellow disk, they will rapidly learn to seek food on a yellow background. If the full dish is now placed on a blue background and an empty dish on the yellow, the bees will continue seeking food on the yellow background. With a careful application of this and other training experiments, we are able to show that bees can distinguish colors (although we do not know *what* they see). In similar ways, it has been shown that at least some teleost fishes can discriminate colors, but elasmobranchs cannot. Turtles, lizards, and birds have color vision, but most mammals, except man and monkeys, are unable to discriminate color.

Sound and Hearing

Sound consists of energy transmitted as waves of compression and decompression in air, liquids, and solids. We can hear frequencies between about 16 and 20,000 cycles per second (cps), but the range may be different for other animals. Dogs can hear sounds above the limit of the human ear: a dog whistle that produces, say, 30,000 cps is audible to the dog but seems silent to us. Bats can both produce and hear sounds up to around 100,000 cps, an ability they use for orientation during flight, much as other animals use their eyes (see pp. 87–89).

The lower limit of hearing is difficult to establish. A fish will sense the steps of a man as he walks on the ground and approaches the edge of the water. Much of the vibration of the steps transmitted from the ground to the water is of very low frequency, and the fish will perceive these vibrations with sensory organs in the lateral line rather than in the ear. Is it then correct to say that the fish "hears" our approach? Although we ourselves can sense vibrations below the limit of hearing, we do not call it hearing because we do not perceive the vibrations as sound. Since it is impossible for us to establish how animals perceive a particular vibration, we like to speak about animals "hearing" only if they have a specially developed organ that is sensitive to sound. When vibrations fall outside of what *we* think is sound, we tend to speak in less well-defined terms and say an animal is "sensitive to vibration," particularly if we cannot point to any specific hearing organ.

Man can *detect* sound waves, determine their *intensity,* distinguish different *frequencies* (pitch), carry out *frequency analysis* of a complicated wave pattern, and also determine the *direction* from which the sound is coming. Experiments with other higher vertebrates indicate that they respond in much the same way as we do, which is not surprising since the structure of their ears is much like ours. It has been claimed that fishes neither can hear nor produce sound, but this is definitely wrong; many fish can produce sounds in various ways, and most can probably hear. Now that we have adequate listening equipment, it has been discovered that the sea in fact is quite noisy, and not only fish but many invertebrates, too, produce sounds. To establish the role of sounds in the life of aquatic animals is, of course, much more difficult, and we still have a tremendous amount to learn about animal sound.

Insects produce a variety of sounds and many of them obviously use sound as a means of communication, often to find the opposite sex. The hearing organs in insects show a great variety of structures and locations —many are in the abdomen and some are even in the antennae. It is very unlikely, judging from the structures, that insect hearing organs are sensitive to change in pitch the way our ear is. If we record and play back the chirps of certain grasshopper males that attract females, with so much frequency distortion that they are unrecognizable to us, they still attract female grasshoppers. It turns out that insect hearing is sensitive to changes in intensity and in the duration and pattern of bursts of sound. The sound wave to insects has a function analogous to that of the carrier wave in radio, and the information that is meaningful to insects is carried in the pattern of pulses, rather than in pitch and tone quality. It is our own inherent inability to appreciate the important features of insect song that has obscured its variety and meaning for so long. Electronic equipment for recording and frequency analysis has enabled us to transfer sound to visual patterns that we can better understand and evaluate.

Odor and Chemical Senses

Man makes a distinction between odor and taste, between smelling and tasting. Since both these senses react to certain chemical substances, they are both designated as *chemoreceptors*. The nose responds to substances in gas form in the air, and the taste is sensitive to substances in solution. The distinction seems clearer than it actually is, for the substances we smell must be dissolved in the surface of the olfactory epithelium before they are perceived. And what about aquatic animals? They definitely have chemical senses, sometimes of great acuity (see the homing of the salmon, p. 90), but do they "smell" or "taste"? A scallop will, when approached by a starfish, take off and swim through the water; should we say that it "smells" or "tastes" the presence of its enemy? In common language, it is convenient to use "smell" for objects at a distance and "taste" for materials in contact with the animals, in particular with the mouth. In scientific terminology, it is better not to make the sharp distinction but to classify all chemical senses as chemoreceptors.

Again, we should realize that the senses of animals are often quite different from ours. Man has rather acute vision and hearing, and he gets most of his information about the world through these two senses. Odors play a minor role in our world; witness the fact that we do not have a common word for the deficiency of smell that corresponds to "blindness" or "deafness." To us, lack of sight and hearing are serious handicaps, but we are not much concerned with a deficiency of smell. Many animals, however, could not survive without the sense of smell, since they could neither find their food nor avoid their enemies.

To understand better the meaning of odors to animals, let us consider the abilities of dogs. Dogs recognize their friends and foes, whether man or animal, by means of smell; they mark off their territory with their own urine, which is individually recognizable to themselves and to other dogs; they can track down and find hidden persons or objects; and they are incredibly acute in distinguishing the odors of different individuals. Interestingly enough, one thing confuses even the best tracking dogs—they are usually unable to distinguish the odors of identical twins.

The acuity of smell in some moths has long been known and admired. The male of certain moths can detect and fly to a female of the same species over a distance of several miles, and the amount of odoriferous substance that reaches the sense organ of the male must be unbelievably small. Collectors know that if they can capture a single female of certain rare species, they can afterwards collect as many males as they wish by using the female as an attraction. The moths have no nose to smell with, but sensitive chemoreceptors are located on the antennae. They do have a "tongue," but "taste" by means of chemoreceptors on their feet (Fig. 6-2).

CONTACT RECEPTORS

The senses that yield information about conditions at the immediate surface of animals are the senses of touch and pressure (*tactile sense*), the sensations of heat and cold (*thermal sense*), and the *chemical sense* (taste)

Fig. 6-2. The butterfly (and the housefly and bee, for that matter) tastes with its feet. If a sugar solution is applied to one of the forelegs, the long hollow mouth, which usually is carried rolled up, immediately stretches out and sucks up the food.

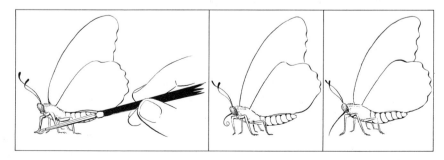

—the latter we have already discussed in connection with the sense of smell. Certain stimuli also evoke *pain,* an ill-defined but clearly felt sensation that may be due to several causes but is usually connected with damaging or deleterious stimuli. A great deal is known about the tactile and thermal senses in man and about the structures responsible for the sensations, and from the responses of animals we know that they are similarly sensitive to tactile and thermal stimuli.

PROPRIOCEPTORS

This term refers to those sense organs that give information about oneself and one's own body, such as the position of the limbs and the orientation of the body in the field of gravity. Although we usually pay no attention to the proprioceptive senses, they are of essential importance, as is spectacularly demonstrated in the difficulties experienced by persons who lose them.

The feeling for the position of the limbs stems from special sense organs imbedded in the muscle. The nerve connected with a muscle does not contain merely fibers that stimulate contraction, but also fibers that come from specialized structures called *muscle spindles.* These are modified muscle fibers, wrapped around with fine nerve fibers and enclosed in a capsule. The muscle spindles are sensitive to the stretch in the muscle (and are thus known as *stretch receptors*) and constantly signal to the central nervous system the position of all muscles. Similar sense organs in the tendons are sensitive to the amount of tension in the tendon, and we speak of them as *tension receptors.* The joints, too, have special receptors of a similar nature.

The position relative to "up" and "down" is, in vertebrates, sensed by the inner ear, which, in addition to the hearing parts, has a complex structure called the *labyrinth* (Fig. 6-3). In the *ampullae,* we find patches of modified sensory epithelium, covered with a mucus that contains numerous small calcareous concretions, called *otoliths* (otos = ear, lithos = stone). As the position of the head changes, the pressure of the otoliths on the sensory epithelium changes accordingly, producing a sensation of position. The three *semicircular canals,* which are located in three different planes with 90° angles between them, are filled with fluid and have a crest of sensory epithelium that responds to movement of this fluid.

Fig. 6-3. In the ear of man, the bones of the middle ear and the cochlea are associated with sound conduction and hearing. The semicircular canals, which are located in three planes perpendicular to each other, perceive changes in motion of the head (kinetic sense), and the ampullae perceive positions relative to up and down (static sense).

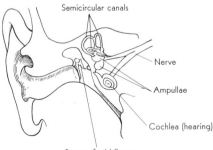

Semicircular canals

Nerve

Ampullae

Cochlea (hearing)

Bones of middle ear
(sound transmission)

When the head is turned, the inertia of the fluid starts it moving relative to the semicircular canal in the plane of movement, and thus the change is perceived. Since the canals are in three different planes, any change will be perceived by one of the canals, or as a combination of effects in all of them. The canals are thus *kinetic* sense organs, since they respond to *motion,* while the ampullae are both *kinetic* and *static* organs, for they respond to linear inertia and orientation.

The type of sense organ in which a heavy particle rests on sensitive cells is also very common in invertebrate animals. The function of these organs was surmised long ago from their structure, and an elegant proof of it was provided in crayfish, where the organs are located at the base of the antennae and are connected to the outside by an open passage. The crayfish's ampullae contain small grains of sand, which are lost when the crayfish changes the exoskeleton during growth. To replace the grains, the crayfish shovels sand over its head until suitable grains enter the ampullae. In an aquarium where the sand is replaced by iron or nickel particles, the crayfish will use these instead. If a magnet is now held above the animal, it will promptly turn upside down; that is, it will orient "properly" according to the pull of the magnetic particle.

In our discussion, we have not mentioned sensory nerve endings in internal organs, such as the intestine, or the chemoreceptors of the aorta, which are sensitive to oxygen concentration. We are not aware of the activity of these receptors (except for pain), so we shall not go into them here.

ORIENTATION AND NAVIGATION

Bat Sonar

Men have long marveled at the ability of bats to catch their insect prey at night and to maneuver in dark caves, where they avoid stalactites and other obstacles. In 1793 the Italian naturalist Spallanzani noticed that when he released a captive owl in his room, the owl became quite helpless after the only lighted candle was blown out. The owl obviously could not see in the dark, but when Spallanzani repeated the experiment with bats, he soon found that even in complete darkness they avoided obstacles and never hit the walls.

Spallanzani first thought his bats were able to see by light that was too dim to be perceived by man or the owl. He tied a hood of opaque material around their heads and noted that they could not avoid obstacles, even in daylight, so he concluded that the eyes were essential for their flight. But later when he blinded bats, whose eyes are poorly developed to begin with, but kept their ears uncovered, he found that they could still avoid obstacles in flight as easily as before. On the other hand, when he plugged the ears of the bats with wax, they became disoriented; plugging only one ear did not make much difference, but if both were plugged, they became almost completely helpless.

Spallanzani was never able to discover how bats orient in flight, and it was not until apparatus designed to detect and record sound waves beyond the hearing range of man had been developed that the full story became known. In 1938 a student at Harvard University brought some bats to a physics professor who had supersonic detecting equipment, and they found that bats emit a wide variety of sounds up to 100,000 cycles per second (the limit for hearing in man is below 20,000 cycles per second). Later work has shown that bats emit short pulses of high-frequency sound, and that the reflections or echoes of these sound pulses tell them the location of solid objects. The system is, in principle, the same as that applied in sonar, which is employed, for example, in the detection of submarines. The devices constructed by man weigh hundreds of pounds, but the immensely more precise system of the bat consists of an ultra-sonic sound generator in the vocal cords and a detector mechanism in the minute structures of the ear, all housed in an animal that weighs less than an ounce.

Small bats (Microchiroptera) all rely on echo-location for orientation, but many of the large bats (Megachiroptera), such as the flying foxes, have no sonar. These are fruit eaters and they fly and feed only in day-light; their prominent eyes indicate that they depend on vision, and if forced to fly in the dark, they are confused and disoriented.

One of the Microchiroptera that has been much studied is the big brown bat (*Eptesicus fuscus*). As this bat cruises around in the dark, it emits high-pitched sound, inaudible to man, that can be picked up by a sensitive microphone and electronically transformed to lower frequencies which we can hear. With such an apparatus, we hear short clicks as the bat flies around, and when it swoops down to catch an insect the number of clicks increases. During the cruising, each sound pulse lasts about 10 to 15 milliseconds, but as the bat nears the insect, the pulses are shortened to less than one millisecond and are emitted at rates as high as 200 pulses per second.

Bats have an advantage when they use high-frequency pulses (short wavelength), because low-frequency waves spread too widely and their reflections are too diffuse to pinpoint accurately the location of objects. Furthermore, in order to reflect sound waves, an object must be above a certain size, and the shorter the wavelengths, the smaller is the minimum size that will reflect. Thus, the highest frequencies permit detection and accurate location of the smallest objects. If bats are permitted to fly in a room criss-crossed with wires, they can maneuver around them unless the wires are very thin. For example, the little brown bat (*Myotis lucifugus*) can detect a wire $\frac{2}{10}$ mm in diameter, but not one that is only $\frac{1}{10}$ mm. The shortest wavelength emitted by this bat is about 3 mm (100,000 cycles per second) and thus the bat can detect wires that are about $\frac{1}{10}$ of a wavelength thick.

The most impressive aspect of the bat's sonar is its ability to discriminate the faint echoes in the presence of other sounds. The reflections are weaker than the sound pulses by a factor of some two thousand. In big caves, such as the Carlsbad Caverns in New Mexico, thousands of bats are flying at the same time, but from the multitude of signals in the same frequency band, each bat seems to be able to hear its own signals and guide itself without confusion. In laboratory attempts to "jam" their orientation with intense sound, bats are still able to find their way and avoid wires 1 mm thick. They thus have an incredible ability to discriminate and analyze acoustic signals and to eliminate "noise."

After the mystery of bat sonar had been clarified, another biological enigma was cleared up. The oil bird, or guacharo, of Central America (*Steatornis caripensis*) lives and nests in deep caves, leaving them only at night for food. The great explorer von Humboldt observed these strange birds in 1799 and was the first to study how they avoid crashing into obstacles and the walls of the dark caves. It was later shown that these birds use a sonar system similar to that of bats, except that their sounds are fully audible to man. The sounds are somewhat like the ticking of a typewriter, and if we plug the birds' ear canals, they lose their sense of orientation in the dark. They can still fly in a lighted room, however, indicating that they can also use their eyes for orientation.

Quite recently it has been discovered that whales may use acoustic means to avoid colliding with objects or with the ocean bottom. Experiments have been carried out in Florida with bottle-nosed dolphins, or porpoises, which are intelligent and playful animals that are easily housed in large tanks. They frequently emit high-pitched, whistling sounds, which can readily be heard by man. When they swam in turbid water they moved freely and avoided contact with submerged objects or rows of bars, even when a man could not see anything beyond a few inches. To be sure that they did not receive visual cues, sheets of rigid, clear plastic were submerged into openings in a net of submerged rods that the porpoises had been using as "doors." Since they avoided the plastic, the only possible conclusion seems to be that they employed acoustic means to locate the obstacles.

One could object that whales usually do not encounter obstacles when they swim freely in the sea, but acoustic "sight" is also valuable in avoiding collision with the bottom and for locating food at depths where no light penetrates. In a tank with turbid water, a trained porpoise will find a dead fish within seconds after it is thrown into the water, even if it lands at the opposite end of the tank. If several porpoises are present, they race for the food and the first one arriving will grab it without hesitation, very different from the way a man would grope around in the murky water trying to find a submerged object.

The Homing of the Salmon

Some time after a young salmon is hatched in a fresh-water stream, it follows the river system down to the ocean, where it spends several years and grows rapidly into a mature fish of considerable size. During the years in the ocean, the salmon travels over great distances, but when it returns to fresh water to spawn, it always goes back to the stream where it was born. How it finds its way back to the same stream, years after leaving it, has been one of the great mysteries of biology. To confirm that salmon *do* return to the stream of their birth, thousands of young salmon have been marked as they descend to a river's mouth, and then checked upon their re-entry. In one of the largest studies ever made, Canadian investigators marked 469,326 young sockeye salmon in the Fraser River. Over the following years, nearly 11,000 of these were recovered in that river as they returned from the ocean, but not one single marked fish was ever found to have strayed into another stream. How do they find their way back from wanderings that take them hundreds and hundreds of miles out to sea? And they don't even seem to enter another river to check if one of its tributaries could be the right place.

The riddle of the migrating salmon is slowly being unraveled by careful physiological studies, and it now appears that the sense of smell guides the fish back to its home stream. Fishes have an extremely sensitive chemoreceptive sense and can learn to distinguish many "odors." By injecting odors into the water of specially designed aquaria, Wisconsin zoologists investigated whether fish could distinguish the odors of different water plants. For responding to the odor of one kind, the fish was rewarded with food; for responding to that of another, it was punished with a weak electric shock (you will note that this is the same principle of reward and punishment used in other investigations of animal senses). Since it was found that the fish could easily be trained to choose between different odors and that they could distinguish dilute rinses of all the different plants that were tested, these experiments suggested that odors might be the clue to the homing ability of the salmon. The next step was to test whether water samples from different streams have characteristic odors that fish can recognize. Comparisons of the waters of various streams revealed that their odors were indeed different, and, when a salmon's olfactory tissue was destroyed or its nose was plugged with cotton, the fish could no longer distinguish odors.

These laboratory results seemed so promising that a field experiment was undertaken. Mature salmon that had returned to spawn were hauled out of two different branches of the Issaquah River in the state of Washington, and were then taken downstream and released. In half the fish, the noses were plugged with cotton; these fish migrated back upstream, but picked the wrong stream as often as the right one, while those with unplugged noses always returned to their home stream. Many later experiments have confirmed these earlier results, and it now seems certain that the sense of smell is the guiding factor in the migration of the salmon to its spawning grounds. The "odor" of the water in which the small salmon hatches is apparently retained in the memory of the fish for its lifetime.

The phenomenon of a very young animal having an experience firmly fixed in its memory throughout its life is a well-known one that, in animal behavior studies, is called *imprinting*.

Imprinting can also involve the sense of sight. For example, those birds, such as ducks, geese, and chickens, that are ready to move about as soon as they are hatched tend to follow the first moving object they see and only that object. Since the first moving body the chicks normally see is the mother leaving the nest, they will follow her and in this way learn the characteristics of their own species. In the mallard, the period of strongest imprinting is from 8 to 16 hours after hatching. The newly hatched duckling is physically unable to travel for some 8 hours, but after that it will follow anything that moves with a suitable speed, even a ping-pong ball pulled by a string. At the end of the imprinting period, it will follow this object in preference to all others, and may not be able to recognize its own species for the rest of its life; it will behave as if the ping-pong ball were its own mother. The mallard will consider the imprinted object as one of its own species, and sometimes will center its sexual attention around this object in its adult life. Thus, the early experiences of an animal may determine all its later life. Could a young salmon be imprinted by what it smells, as a young chick is imprinted by what it sees?

Integration

CHAPTER SEVEN

All functions in an organism are accurately controlled and adjusted, are correlated with the function of other organs, and are integrated according to the needs of the entire body. We have already seen that there are several ways of controlling physiological function. The contraction of the diaphragm during inspiration is controlled by a nerve from the respiratory center. The secretion of digestive juices from the pancreas is stimulated by a hormone (secretin), which is released from the wall of the upper intestine. Thus, both nerves and hormones control body processes, and even a metabolic product as simple as carbon dioxide has, as we have discussed, an important part in the control of respiration.

As we examine the various functions of the body, we find a variety of different controlling processes. Some general principles, however, are evident. Where a rapid response is required, such as stimulation of skeletal muscles, nerves are necessary because of their rapid rate of conduction. Nerve impulses can move with a speed of several hundred feet per second, and thus only milliseconds will elapse before the effect takes place. |When a process is regulated by a hormone, on the other hand, the response cannot begin before the hormone reaches the target organ via the blood stream, so the time for a response to occur will be, at best, a fraction of a minute, and is usually longer.| Processes that are under hormonal control, therefore, are those in which an instantaneous response is not needed, such as the pancreatic secretion, the control of urine volume, the excretion of sodium, or even such slower processes as growth of the body and development of the reproductive organs. We shall find, however, that there is no sharp division between nervous and hormonal control, although, for the sake of clarity, we shall begin with one and discuss the other subsequently.

STRUCTURE OF THE NERVOUS SYSTEM

In vertebrates, the nervous system consists of the brain, the spinal cord, and the nerves that connect these central portions with all parts of the body. In order to understand how the various parts work, we must have some knowledge of the structure and function of the individual nerve cell. This chapter will therefore first describe the *nerve cell* and its parts. Next we shall briefly discuss the high command—the brain and the spinal cord— which are usually referred to as the *central nervous system*. It receives information from various sensory organs through nerves which are called *sensory nerves*. The central nervous system also sends impulses to the various parts of the body. Some nerves are under the control of the will and stimulate striated muscle, 'and since these nerves involve motion, they are termed *motor nerves*. Another set of nerves that is extremely important although not under voluntary control is the *autonomic nervous system,* which regulates the function of internal organs such as the digestive glands, the heart, the intestine, etc.

THE NERVE CELL AND ITS PARTS. The entire nervous system is made up of single nerve cells called *neurons* (Fig. 7-1). Each neuron consists of an irregular cell body, which contains the nucleus, and several thin fibers

Fig. 7-1. Two types of nerve cells. Top, bipolar sensory nerve; bottom, motor nerve cell from spinal cord. Compare with the schematic diagram of a spinal reflex in Fig. 7-2.

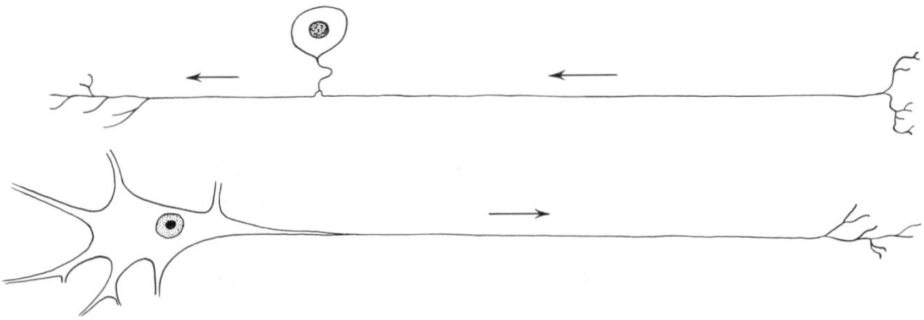

extending from it. The fibers are often less than 0.01 mm thick; most of them are relatively short, up to a few millimeters long, and are frequently branched. One of the fibers is often much longer and may extend for a meter or more. What we call a nerve consists of hundreds or thousands of nerve fibers, each belonging to a different neuron. The nerve has no cell bodies in it, for these bodies are located in the brain and spinal cord or in aggregations in other parts of the body that are called *ganglia* (ganglion means swelling).

The nerve cells make contact with each other through their fibers at connections called *synapses*. A great deal is known about the transmission of impulses in the single nerve fiber and about the synaptic transmission from one cell to another, but our understanding of the function of the central nervous system is less adequate. The nervous system of a man contains something like ten billion nerve cells, and the branching nerve fibers from each connect with numerous other cells in a system of inconceivable complexity that makes it virtually impossible to know in full detail what takes place in the central nervous system.

THE CENTRAL NERVOUS SYSTEM.   The largest part of the brain in higher vertebrates, the *cerebrum,* contains the so-called higher centers. Partly by experimentation on animals and partly by observation of the effects of brain injury in man, it has been possible to establish that the cerebrum, and in particular its outer part, the *cortex,* is the seat of conscious perception, association, and thinking. Specific areas have been found to be associated with sight, hearing, the ability to speak, the movements of the various parts of the body, and so on.

In previous chapters we have several times referred to the important functions of the *hypothalamus.* In this area are located automatic regulations such as the temperature regulation center, the center that is responsible for the regulation of food intake, for thirst and drinking, and many others. Below the hypothalamus is the *hypophysis* (or *pituitary*), one of the most important hormone-producing glands in the body. The *spinal cord* is a direct continuation of the brain, running down the length of the vertebral column.

A total of twelve pairs of nerves, called *cranial nerves,* leave the brain and lead to various parts of the body. At the level of each vertebra, a set of *spinal nerves* leaves the spinal cord. These nerves supply all the lower parts of the body; if we sense a pain in the index finger, for example, the sensation is first transmitted to the level of the seventh vertebra of the neck, and from here it travels to the brain. And if we decide to move the hands, the impulse travels from the brain to the appropriate segment of the spinal cord and on out through the motor nerves to the muscles in question. The spinal cord, however, is not completely under the control of the brain, for it has a great deal of autonomy, as we shall see later when we discuss *spinal reflexes.*

SENSORY NERVES. The nerves that conduct impulses to the central nervous system are called sensory nerves. They convey impulses from all sensory organs, both those that we are aware of and those that do not come to conscious realization. The major sense organs are connected directly with the brain nerves: Impulses from the olfactory sense are transmitted in the *olfactory* (first cranial) nerve; the *optic* (second cranial) nerve is connected with the *retina* of the eye; impulses from the forehead, scalp, upper eyelid, nose, and teeth are conveyed in the *trigeminal* (fifth cranial) nerve—this nerve is not only sensory but contains motor nerves as well and thus conducts both to and from the brain (each fiber, of course, conducts only one kind of information and in one direction only); the *facial* (seventh cranial) nerve is also a mixed nerve, of which the sensory part conveys *taste;* the *acoustic* (eighth cranial) nerve conveys *hearing* and the sense of *equilibrium* from the inner ear; the *glossopharyngeal* (ninth) is mixed, the sensory part conveying *taste* and *touch;* the tenth cranial nerve, the *vagus,* which is an extremely important nerve and has connections to most of the internal organs, is also a mixed nerve.

Sensory impulses from the lower part of the body reach the spinal cord before they are conveyed to the brain. These impulses originate from receptors in the skin, in the stretch receptors in muscles and tendons, in the nerve endings in the internal organs, etc. Usually, very little of the information from the internal organs comes to conscious sensation, with the exception of pain.

MOTOR NERVES. The nerves that convey impulses from the central nervous system can be divided into those under voluntary control that supply skeletal or striated muscles, and those not subject to voluntary control that carry all other outgoing impulses. Although all striated muscle can be consciously controlled, most of its activity never reaches conscious realization; for example, the complex movements of breathing and walking take place without our thinking about them.

The simplest way that movements can occur without the intervention of the higher centers is illustrated in the *spinal reflex.* An excellent example of such a reflex is the well-known knee-jerk reflex, which occurs if we lightly hit the knee of the bent leg just below the kneecap. The pathway for the reflex is given in diagram form in Fig. 7-2. The light tap on the tendon causes it to stretch rapidly, thus stimulating stretch receptors that immediately send impulses through the sensory nerves toward the spinal cord. The impulse reaches the nerve cell body in the dorsal root and continues to the spinal cord, where it connects to several other neurons. These immediately send impulses in the ventral root, which contains the motor fibers to the muscle that is connected with the same tendon, causing the muscle to contract. Simple spinal reflexes are very useful; for example, if we accidently put our hand on a hot stove, it is withdrawn before we even realize that heat and pain are involved.

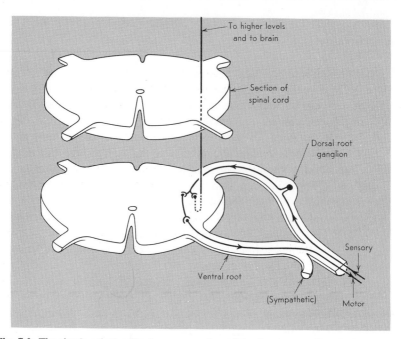

Fig. 7-2. The simple spinal reflex in a mammal consists of a sensory fiber in the dorsal root, which connects with one or several nerve cells in the spinal cord, and a motor fiber in the ventral root. The spinal nerves in other vertebrates are arranged in a similar but not identical pattern.

The simple spinal reflex is rarely as simple as it sounds from this description. The incoming nerve fiber connects not only to motor neurons, but to several neurons that have connections up and down the spinal cord and thus lead to the other parts of the central nervous system, including the cortex of the brain. Movements of the limbs require not only the orderly contraction of certain muscles, but also a reflex relaxation of antagonistic muscles. Even quite simple organized movements, therefore, involve a complex system of inhibition as well as stimulation of nerve cells in the spinal cord.

THE AUTONOMIC NERVOUS SYSTEM. The autonomic nervous system is that part of the peripheral nervous system which is not under the control of the will. Like most definitions, this one is not entirely accurate, for a reflex such as the knee-jerk is involuntary, although it does not involve the autonomic nervous system. The difference is that the muscles of the leg can also be controlled voluntarily, whereas none of the organs innervated by the autonomic nervous system—the heart, stomach, digestive glands, intestine, and so on—can be controlled as we wish.

Figure 7-3 gives a schematic view of the structure of the autonomic nervous system. Autonomic fibers are found in the third, seventh, ninth, and tenth cranial nerves (the tenth is the very important *vagus nerve*); the spinal nerves have no autonomic fibers in the region of the neck, but the lower regions have autonomic fibers for each segment. There is an interesting difference in the structure of motor nerves and autonomic nerves. The cell bodies of the motor neurons are always located in the central nervous system, and the long nerve fibers run uninterruptedly all the way to the muscle. The fibers of the autonomic nervous system also originate in neurons inside the central system, but they always run to another nerve cell outside the central nervous system where they form a synapse, and a second fiber carries the impulse on to the effector.

Functional peculiarities of the autonomic nervous system separate it into two parts. One, the *parasympathetic system,* consists of nerves from the brain and from the sacral region of the spinal cord. The secondary ganglia in this system are located far from the central nervous system, frequently in the immediate vicinity of or even inside the target organ. The other part of the autonomic nervous system, the *sympathetic* system, originates in the thoracic and lumbar parts of the spinal cord, and the nerves form a set of ganglia immediately outside the vertebral column, the so-called *sympathetic chain.* The secondary, or post-ganglionic, fibers

Fig. 7-3. The autonomic nervous system consists of two parts, the parasympathetic and the sympathetic systems. Most internal organs receive fibers from both. For clarity, the two systems have been drawn separately in this diagram.

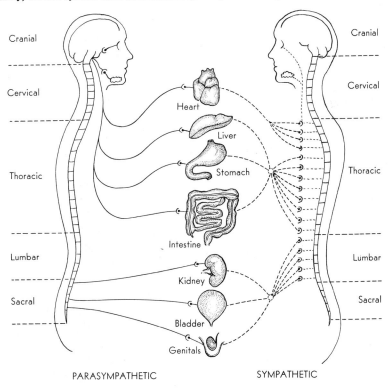

PARASYMPATHETIC   SYMPATHETIC

continue from the sympathetic chain to the target organs, sometimes forming additional synapses in other ganglia on their way.

All the internal organs receive fibers from the parasympathetic as well as from the sympathetic systems, and the fibers of the two systems have opposite effects on the organ—if one is stimulating, the other is inhibitory. When we discussed the rate of the heart beat, we found that it is inhibited by the vagus nerve and accelerated by the sympathetic nerve. We also observed that these nerves act on the heart by releasing chemicals; the parasympathetic nerve (vagus) releases acetylcholine, and the sympathetic nerve releases adrenalin. With very few exceptions, all sympathetic endings release noradrenalin and the similar adrenalin, and all parasympathetic endings release acetylcholine. Adrenalin is not always stimulating, and acetylcholine is not always inhibitory; for example, the salivary glands are stimulated by the parasympathetic nerve and inhibited by the sympathetic. Acetylcholine is a substance of great importance in the transmission of impulses in the synapses, and adrenalin is an important hormone that we shall discuss later. At that time we shall present an easy rule-of-thumb for remembering which functions are stimulated and which are inhibited by adrenalin or sympathetic nerves.

TRANSMISSION OF THE NERVE IMPULSE

TRANSMISSION IN THE NERVE FIBER.   We have seen that when a stimulus travels in a motor nerve to a muscle, the fibers contract when the impulse arrives. We can, therefore, recognize the impulse by its effect, but we have not yet discussed the impulse and what it really is.   The easiest way to discover that an impulse passes in a nerve is to measure the electric changes in the nerve fiber. If fine electrodes are placed on the surface of a resting nerve fiber, no difference in electrical potential can be detected between them, but when an impulse travels along the fiber an instantaneous change occurs, caused by the movement of ions in the surface of the nerve (see p. 100). If we apply electronic amplifiers to the minute currents, we can record them. Figure 7-4 shows the potential as it can be recorded between one electrode placed on the surface and one placed inside the fiber. The change in potential developed during the

Fig. 7-4. A record of the electrical events associated with a nerve impulse. As the impulse passes a point on the nerve fiber, this point on the surface momentarily becomes negative in relation to the rest of the surface. Note that the negative potential is indicated upwards. Each time cycle is 1/1000 sec.

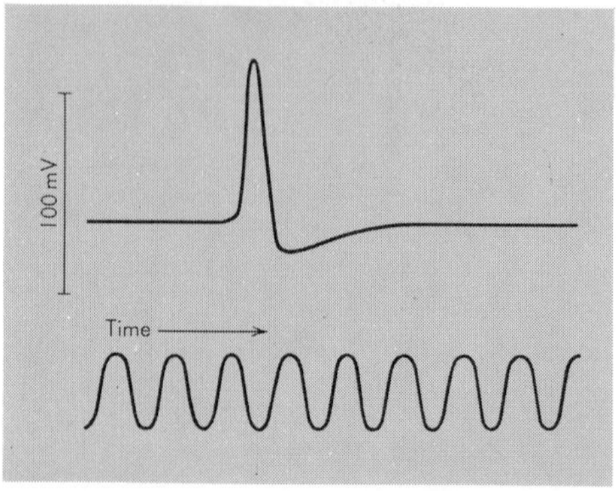

brief period of activity is called the *action potential,* but we must point out that the action potential is not the nerve impulse itself; it is only a means of showing that something does happen. If an automobile travels down a highway, we can follow it by recording the noise as the car passes, but the sound itself is not the automobile. A suitable receiver could also pick up the radio waves transmitted by the spark plugs of the car, and here the record would give the electrical phenomena associated with the event, which is a situation analogous to that in our experiment. As a nerve impulse travels down the nerve, there are other changes such as heat production, consumption of oxygen, carbon dioxide production, movement of ions, and so on, but these we cannot measure as easily as we can the electric ones.

To find out more about transmission in nerve fibers, we produce impulses in fibers that have been isolated for study. Many different stimuli will initiate impulses, which are then propagated in the fiber: Pinching the nerve will do this; applying a tiny drop of acid or a strong salt solution will also do it; but the most suitable stimulus is a small electric current. Electricity can be applied instantaneously in an accurately measured amount, for a short and measurable time, and it can be removed instantaneously. Electric stimuli also have very little or no damaging effect on a nerve fiber, whereas the other stimuli we mentioned soon would leave the nerve useless for further experimentation.

When we stimulate a nerve fiber, we find that very weak stimuli give no response at all, and thus, as in the case of muscle, there is a *threshold value* or rheobase below which no reaction takes place. Above the threshold, a stimulus always gives the same magnitude of impulse, irrespective of the strength of the stimulus. Here again we have a case of the *all-or-none rule;* when conditions are otherwise unchanged (temperature, oxygen supply, etc.), the impulse is independent of the strength of the stimulus, once the threshold is exceeded. If we measure the magnitude of the nerve impulse as it travels along the nerve fiber, we shall find that it does not decrease in magnitude, for, unlike a pulse of electricity running in a conductor where the resistance gradually diminishes the current, the nerve impulse is, as we say, conducted *without decrement.*

In the body, the nerve impulses in a given fiber always travel in the same direction. Can the fibers only conduct in one direction? If we apply a stimulus in the middle of a long nerve fiber, we see that the impulse spreads in both directions at equal speed. In the body, however, the flow of impulses is unidirectional, because the synapses will permit passage in one direction only. For example, if we were to stimulate artificially the motor fiber in the simple spinal reflex, the impulse would reach the nerve cell in the spinal cord, but it would stop here because the synapses with the dorsal root do not permit passage in that direction. Thus, it is the synaptic connection that acts as a unidirectional valve, with the result that any given fiber transmits in one direction only.

A nerve impulse moves very rapidly, up to over 100 meters per second, but this is still much slower than the propagation of electricity in conductors, which approaches the speed of light (300,000 kilometers per second). The rate of conduction in a nerve usually is higher in warm-blooded animals than in cold-blooded ones, and higher in fast-moving than in slow-moving animals (Table 7-1). The diameter of the fiber also determines the rate of conduction; the larger fibers conduct faster. The extreme case of this is found in those animals that have *giant fibers,* which may be up to one millimeter in diameter. In the squid, for example, giant fibers run the length of the mantle, and their function is to transmit more rapidly than ordinary nerves when the animal needs to move quickly. From Table 7-1 you can see that the giant fibers conduct much faster than do the regular nerves in the same animal.

This arrangement, in which a few fibers are ten or a hundred times as thick as normal ones, is a biological curiosity, but a very important one, for it has supplied physiologists with excellent material for experiments. Nerve fibers of this size are relatively rugged, can easily be handled, are large enough so that electrodes can be placed on the surface and inside, contain enough material for chemical analysis, and, since they are from cold-blooded animals, do not have to be kept warm in order to behave normally.

Experiments with giant fibers have revealed a great similarity between nerve and muscle; in fact, the similarity is so great that we could use the diagram of a muscle fiber in Fig. 5-4 to describe the nerve, with only slight changes in the legend. The surface of the nerve has a positive charge of about 0.1 volt relative to the inside; during the passage of the impulses the charge is abolished and then re-established by active extrusion of sodium.

Table 7-1

RATES OF CONDUCTION IN THE MOTOR NERVES OF VARIOUS ANIMALS

Animal	Rate (meters/second)
Mammals	30–120
Snake	10–35
Bullfrog	7–30
Fish	50–60
Crab	3.5
Cockroach	1.5–6
Cockroach, giant fibers	9–12
Squid	4.3
Squid, giant fibers	18–35
Earthworm	0.6
Earthworm, giant fibers	10–30
Snail	0.4

The nerve impulse does not last very long, only a few milliseconds, and for a given nerve the duration of the impulse is constant. How, then, can a sensory nerve that is continuously stimulated (e.g., a nerve-ending in the skin) transmit a continuous signal? Since the impulses have constant magnitude and constant duration, the only way of transmitting a continued stimulation is by a train of impulses, one following the other. Investigations have shown that an increase in stimulus gives an increase in the frequency of the nerve impulses. Thus, although the nerve fiber follows the all-or-none rule, it can in this fashion transmit changes in the intensity of the stimulus.

TRANSMISSION FROM CELL TO CELL. In the synapse, a nerve impulse is transmitted from one nerve cell to another. Where a motor fiber reaches a muscle, impulses are transmitted from its end to a muscle cell. Near its end, the motor fiber divides into several branches, and each one of these connects to a muscle fiber. The region of contact is called the *myoneural junction* or the *motor end-plate*. This end-plate has some peculiar properties, one being that there is a delay of a few milliseconds between the arrival of a nerve impulse and the contraction of the muscle fiber. When the nerve impulse reaches the end-plate, acetylcholine is released and acts as a chemical transmitter which causes depolarization of the fiber and contraction. If the acetylcholine were not removed again, it would accumulate and make further transmission impossible. However, an enzyme, *acetylcholinesterase,* which is present at the end-plate, causes an almost instantaneous hydrolysis of the acetylcholine.

Since the acetylcholine is destroyed so rapidly, its brief presence cannot be shown by ordinary means, but if the cholinesterase action is inhibited, the acetylcholine remains at the end-plate and gradually accumulates.* If such a muscle is perfused with saline, acetylcholine appears in the saline when the nerve is stimulated. The amounts of acetylcholine are so small that they are difficult to demonstrate by chemical means, but the heart of the ordinary clam is so sensitive to acetylcholine that it will respond to as little as 0.001 mg in one liter of fluid.

It has been more difficult to demonstrate that acetylcholine is a transmitter substance in the synapse, although work with various drugs that interfere with the action of acetylcholine and cholinesterase indicates that all synapses in the autonomic nervous system (including the sympathetic system) depend on acetylcholine as the transmitter substance. The terminal transmitter substances in the sympathetic system, of course, are adrenalin and noradrenalin.

In the central nervous system, acetylcholine does not play the same role in synaptic transmission as it does outside. If a common chemical

---

* Some of the so-called "nerve gases" are cholinesterase inhibitors and therefore block impulse transmission in the nervous system. One of them, DFP (di-isopropyl-fluorophosphate) has been valuable in helping to clarify the processes in the end-plate.

transmitter substance exists in the central nervous system, we do not yet know its nature. Several substances that contain nitrogen, chemically classed as amines, are found in the central nervous system in relatively high concentration; they have profound physiological effects, but their specific roles remain to be clarified. One of these, *gamma amino butyric acid,* seems to be an inhibitory substance, rather than a stimulating one. We therefore have the fascinating prospect that the normal function of the central nervous system may depend on several transmitter substances, some stimulatory and others inhibitory.

THE NERVOUS SYSTEM AS ORIGINATOR OF HORMONES

ADRENAL MEDULLA. When we discussed the autonomic nervous system, we mentioned that all the autonomic fibers that leave the central nervous system go through at least one additional synapse before they reach the target organ. There is one exception to this; the nerve to the adrenal gland has no intermediate ganglion. The medulla, or central part, of the adrenal develops from neural cells in the embryo and can therefore be regarded as equivalent to the post-ganglionic neurons in the sympathetic system. These cells release a mixture of adrenalin and noradrenalin, which circulates with the blood to all parts of the body. Adrenalin is therefore a hormone, a hormone being a substance which is released by a discrete structure in one part of the body and has an effect somewhere else.

The effect of adrenalin in the blood is similar to a stimulation of the entire sympathetic nervous system. Adrenalin is released during emotions of fear and rage, and since it causes many changes that help the body yield maximum performance, it has been described as an "emergency" or a "fight or flight" hormone. The heart rate increases, the blood pressure goes up, sugar is mobilized from glycogen stored in the liver, and thus the muscles are better supplied with oxygen and glucose. The arterioles in the muscles and heart are dilated, but arterioles in the stomach and intestine are constricted, thus diverting blood to more important organs. This picture gives us an easy way to remember the effects of sympathetic stimulation, and, since they often are opposite, the effects of the parasympathetic system as well. Organs not essential in the "fight or flight" situation— salivary glands, stomach, pancreas, intestine, etc.—are stimulated by parasympathetic and inhibited by sympathetic nerves.

We have now seen that the adrenal medulla produces a hormone that is identical to a nerve transmitter substance. The effects of sympathetic stimulation and adrenalin are quite similar; but the effect from nervous stimulation is almost instantaneous, whereas the hormone cannot act faster than the blood can carry it to the target organ. Furthermore, the sympathetic stimulation can be restricted to a single organ, whereas hormone release affects all functions sensitive to it.

THE NEUROHYPOPHYSIS. Immediately under the hypothalamus and connected with it is a small organ called the *hypophysis* (or *pituitary*). It consists of two parts, the *neurohypophysis* and the *adenohypophysis* (*adenos* means gland). The adenohypophysis, which develops from the roof of the mouth, is in many mammals located in front of the neurohypophysis, and is therefore also called the anterior hypophysis. The posterior part, the neurohypophysis, develops from the brain and consists of modified nerve cells. For the moment, we shall only be concerned with the neurohypophysis and its hormones. The neurohypophysis releases at least two specific hormones; one, *vasopressin,* constricts arterioles and causes a marked rise in blood pressure. The effect lasts much longer than that of adrenalin, about a half hour, whereas the adrenalin effect wears off in a few minutes. Vasopressin is a polypeptide that consists of eight amino acids and is thus entirely different from adrenalin, which is an amine. Vasopressin also brings about a reduction in urine volume by causing the kidney tubules to withhold more water. It was previously believed that this antidiuretic effect was due to a different hormone, called *antidiuretic hormone* (ADH), but it is now clear that the two are identical. Both names are still used, however. Another hormone produced in the neurohypophysis is *oxytocin,* which also is a polypeptide with eight amino acids. This hormone causes contraction of the muscle of the uterus in a pregnant female and is probably released from the neurohypophysis when the pregnancy nears normal term, thereby starting the process of birth. Oxytocin has been used, when necessary, to induce labor.

The parts of the brain that adjoin the hypophysis (certain parts of the hypothalamus in particular) contain large amounts of the same hormones. They are probably produced there and transported in nerve fibers to the neurohypophysis, where they are stored. The function of the neurohypophysis may therefore be one of storage and release of the hormones, rather than one of production. That parts of the nervous system have such important roles in hormone production makes us realize how close the connection is between the two ways of regulating body functions.

MORE HORMONES AND CHEMICAL REGULATORS

The approximate location of hormone-producing organs in mammals is indicated in Fig. 7-5. If the hormone-producing tissue forms a well-defined structure, which has no other apparent function, we call it an *endocrine gland*. An endocrine gland releases the hormone directly into the blood and therefore has no duct, as does, for example, a salivary gland. The hypophysis, thyroid, and adrenal are typical ductless glands; other tissues, such as the intestinal wall, the kidney cortex, etc., have other functions beside hormone production, but this does not detract from the importance of the hormones they produce.

If a tissue is suspected of having endocrine function and of produc-

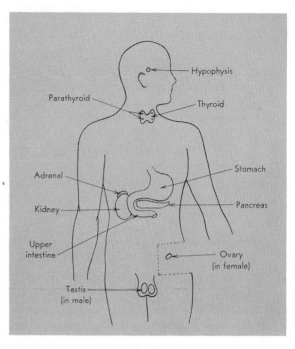

Fig. 7-5. The location of the most important hormone-producing organs.

ing hormones, investigations usually follow these methods: (1) The organ is removed, thus depriving the organism of the normal source of the hormone, so that, as a result, abnormalities and deficiency symptoms should occur; (2) the deficiency symptoms are relieved by replacement therapy, usually by the injection of extracts of the organ that was removed—if this works, purification of the extract may lead to the chemical isolation of the hormone; (3) the deficiency symptoms are treated by the transplantation of hormone-producing tissue from another animal to the experimental animal; (4) finally, the normal role of hormones, particularly in man where experimentation is not readily carried out, is clarified by observations of spontaneous defects in hormone production. These general methods of hormone research sound quite simple, but they have frequently met with great difficulties. Progress in hormone research is slow, for one reason because some organs, such as the hypophysis, contain a number of hormones. Another reason is that many hormone-producing tissues have other roles as well (e.g., the kidney), and the removal of the organ has effects besides removing the hormone source.

A list of some of the most important hormones is given in Table 7-2. The listing is according to the main function of the hormones rather than their anatomical origin. There is actually no sharp separation between the groups, for many hormones have several functions, and there is also a considerable amount of mutual interaction between hormone-producing tissues. Since we have already discussed some of the listed hormones in preceding chapters, we will give only a very brief summary of their functions.

Table 7-2

THE MOST IMPORTANT HORMONES
IN MAMMALS, LISTED IN GROUPS OF RELATED FUNCTION

Area of function	Name	Source	Affects
Circulation	Adrenalin	Adrenal medulla	Blood pressure
	Angiotensin	(see text)	Blood pressure
	Vasopressin	Neurohypophysis	Blood pressure
	Serotonin (= 5-hydroxy-tryptamine)	Blood platelets	Blood pressure intestinal motility
	Histamine	Damaged tissue	Capillary permeability, secretion of HCl in stomach
Glands	Gastrin	Stomach	Gastric secretion
	Secretin	Upper intestine	Pancreatic secretion
	ADH[1] (= vasopressin)	Neurohypophysis	Kidney, urine volume
	Aldosterone	Adrenal cortex	Kidney, Na excretion
Metabolism and Growth	Parathormone	Parathyroid	Ca metabolism
	Insulin	Pancreas	Sugar metabolism
	Glucagon	"	Sugar metabolism
	Thyroxin	Thyroid	Metabolic rate, growth
	Growth hormone	Adenohypophysis	Growth
Reproduction	FSH[2]	Adenohypophysis	Ovary, follicle
	Luteinizing hormone	"	Ovary, corpus luteum
	Prolactin	"	Mammary glands
	Androgen	Adrenal cortex	Male gonads
	Estrogen	Ovary	Female organs
	Progesterone	"	Gestation
	Testosterone	Testis	Male organs
	Oxytocin	Neurohypophysis	Uterus muscle
Endocrine Glands	Thyrotropic hormone	Adenohypophysis	Thyroid
	ACTH[3]	"	Adrenal cortex
	Diabetogenic hormone	"	Pancreas
	Steroid hormones	Adrenal cortex	Most or all endocrine function

[1] Commonly used abbreviation for antidiuretic hormone.
[2] Commonly used abbreviation for follicle-stimulating hormone.
[3] Commonly used abbreviation for adrenocorticotropic hormone.

HORMONES AFFECTING CIRCULATION.   The roles of *adrenalin* and *noradrenalin* as hormones and transmitter substances, discussed above, emphasize the close connection between hormonal and nervous control.

Angiotensin was discovered in experiments in which a clamp was placed on the kidney artery, thus decreasing the blood pressure in the kidney. The kidney responds by releasing to the blood a substance, *renin,* which acts on another substance in the blood to form angiotensin (a polypeptide with eight amino acids). Angiotensin causes the blood pressure to increase as a compensation for the decrease in pressure in the kidney. Since normal kidney function depends on the blood pressure, this compensating mechanism is an automatic feed-back system that is useful in maintaining constant conditions in the kidney.

Vasopressin, released by the neurohypophysis, as we have seen, causes an increase in blood pressure more extended in time than the effect of adrenalin. This hormone is also a polypeptide with eight amino acids, but otherwise is rather different from angiotensin.

If the serum from coagulated blood is injected into an animal, the animal's blood pressure increases because of the presence of *serotonin* (5-hydroxytryptamine), which apparently has been released from broken-down blood platelets. Serotonin's normal role in the organism is not clear. In addition to its effect on blood pressure, it influences the movements of the intestine, and, when injected, is taken up by the blood platelets (which are important in blood coagulation). Serotonin may also have a function in the central nervous system, which is suggested by the fact that part of the molecule of lysergic acid, a substance that causes mental states similar to schizophrenia, is the same as serotonin.

Histamine is a substance with profound physiological effects. Its normal function in an organism is not known, but it plays a part in the body's re-action to harmful influences. Histamine is released from damaged tissues and causes extreme capillary dilation, making the capillary wall permeable even to proteins. Histamine is involved in allergic reactions, which to some extent can be controlled by drugs that prevent its release, the so-called antihistamines. Since an injection of histamine causes secretion of hydro-chloric acid in the stomach, it has been suggested that histamine may be a transmitter substance for the nerves that stimulate acid production, but final proof that histamine is a transmitter substance is still lacking. Hista-mine may also play an unknown role in the central nervous system; anti-histamines tend to prevent seasickness and other forms of motion sickness caused by an overstimulation of certain parts of the hypothalamus.

HORMONES THAT AFFECT GLANDS. In the chapter on food we have already discussed *gastrin,* which stimulates the secretion of gastric juice, and *secretin,* which stimulates the pancreas. These hormones are polypeptides, but we still do not know their exact structures.

The *antidiuretic hormone,* which increases the reabsorption of water in the kidney and thus reduces the volume of urine, is identical to vasopressin.

Aldosterone belongs to a group of chemical substances known as steroids. Several dozen different steroids have been isolated from the adrenal cortex and many of them have physiological effects, but others seem inactive and may be either precursors or metabolic products of those that are active. (It is interesting that vitamin D is also a steroid.) Aldosterone, which can be isolated from the adrenal cortex, influences sodium excretion in the kidney, and in its absence large amounts of sodium are excreted. If the adrenals are removed from rats, the animals usually survive if given a 1 per cent solution of sodium chloride instead of drinking water (the loss of the adrenalin production does not seem to be very serious). Such rats turn out to be quite sensitive to chilling; normal rats easily maintain their body temperature at freezing temperature, but those without adrenals soon succumb to cold. The adrenal cortex is also important in the resistance to other types of stress.

HORMONES WITH A METABOLIC ROLE. *Parathormone* is produced by the parathyroid glands, which are located near, or even imbedded in, the thyroid gland. It regulates the metabolism of calcium and phosphate. Removal of the parathyroids is followed by tetanic muscle cramps, caused by a fall in blood calcium concentration. Excess of the hormone causes increased blood calcium and abnormally high calcium excretion, and the bones become decalcified because they supply the extra calcium drained from the organism.

The human disease known as *diabetes mellitus,* or simply diabetes, results from a decrease in the production of *insulin* in the pancreas. The pancreas, in addition to the cells that produce pancreatic juice, contains groups of entirely different cells, the Langerhans islets, which produce insulin. The most obvious effect of insulin is that it increases the transformation of blood glucose to glycogen, which is deposited in liver and muscle as reserve carbohydrate. In the diabetic with too little insulin, the blood glucose is too high, and glucose appears in the urine. Injection of insulin increases the glycogen deposition and glucose disappears from the urine, but excessive doses decrease the blood glucose to values below that required for normal body functions and may be dangerous or even fatal. Insulin is a protein that consists of 51 amino acids, and it was the first protein whose exact structure was known, owing largely to the spectacular chemical detective work of English biochemists.

Another hormone, *glucagon,* has more recently been discovered in the pancreas. It is produced by the so-called alpha cells of the Langerhans islets, whereas insulin is produced by the beta cells. By causing an increase in the transformation of glycogen into glucose and increasing the blood glucose level, it has the opposite effect of insulin, thus complicating the evaluation of the diabetic patient. A further complication is caused by a hormone produced in the hypophysis, the *diabetogenic hormone,* which affects the hormone production of the pancreas.

Thyroxin is produced by the thyroid gland. If larger-than-normal amounts of the hormone are released from the gland, it causes an increase in the resting metabolism and oxygen consumption, whereas a deficiency decreases the metabolic rate to levels below normal. Thyroxin also affects growth; a deficiency stunts growth and results in a dwarf whose mental development is also retarded.

One interesting role of the thyroid gland is in the metamorphosis of tadpoles. If tadpoles have their thyroids removed, they will not transform into adult frogs, but if they are injected with thyroid hormone, or simply fed some thyroid gland, they will transform. If they are given thyroid before they should normally change, they will develop prematurely into midget adults.

The thyroid hormone is an amino acid that contains several atoms of iodine, and therefore iodine is necessary for its formation. In some regions (around the Great Lakes and in the Pacific Northwest), the iodine content of the soil is so low that it may affect entire populations. The addition of a minute amount of iodine to the table salt has virtually eliminated this type of thyroid deficiency.

The adenohypophysis produces a hormone, called the *growth hormone,* that is responsible for normal growth. A deficiency in this hormone produces a dwarf, who, since in other respects he is quite normal, is not the same type as that produced by a thyroid deficiency. An excess of the growth hormone causes abnormal growth and the development of oversized individuals. Both types of abnormality occur in man in connection with malfunction of the hypophysis.

ROLE OF HORMONES IN THE REPRODUCTIVE ORGANS.   Hormones have a profound role in the development of the gonads and in reproduction. A large number of endocrine substances are secreted by the gonads and the hypophysis, and their interactions still remain obscure on several points. Even a superficial discussion of this subject would require a chapter outside the scope of this book, but the subject is fascinating, and the interested reader is referred to one of the more comprehensive treatments listed in the Selected Readings at the end of the book.

In man, the gonads of the young individual remain dormant until the age of about 10 to 14, when they are stimulated by *gonadotropic hormones* from the adenohypophysis. At that age, for reasons not yet understood, the adenohypophysis begins to secrete two hormones, the *follicle-stimulating hormone (FSH)* and the *luteinizing hormone (LH).*

In the female, FSH induces the ovary to form a follicle with a maturing egg, hence its name. When the egg has been released, the LH causes the remains of a follicle to change into a *corpus luteum,* which means a "yellow body." If pregnancy occurs, the corpus luteum secretes other hormones, primarily *progesterone* which is responsible for the changes in the female during gestation. If pregnancy does not occur, the thickened epithelium of the uterus sloughs off (menstruation), a new egg follicle ripens, and the cycle is repeated.

In the male, the FSH promotes the formation of *sperm,* and the LH stimulates the function of the *interstitial cells* that are located in between the tissues that produce sperm. The interstitial cells, in turn, produce *testosterone,* which is responsible for adult development of the male reproductive organs, deep voice, growth of beard, etc.

HORMONES THAT AFFECT ENDOCRINE GLANDS.   In the preceding paragraphs, we have several times mentioned the effects of some endocrine glands on the functioning of others. In particular, the adenohypophysis affects the reproductive glands in a significant way and it also has other stimulating functions, two of which deserve further mention. In the first place, the adenohypophysis produces a hormone, *thyrotropic hormone,* that stimulates the activity of the thyroid gland. An increased amount of thyroxin in the blood, in turn, inhibits the release of thyrotropic hormone from the adenohypophysis, and thus the interaction between these two glands results in the automatic maintenance of a balanced secretion of both hormones.

Another hormone from the adenohypophysis is ACTH, or *adrenocorticotropic hormone,* a protein that has recently received a great deal of attention in connection with its action on the adrenal cortex and the physiological defense mechanisms of the body. We mentioned before that the adrenal cortex is vital to the body's resistance to cold and certain other types of stress. Although ACTH is undoubtedly a crucial factor in the delicate balance of hormones, we do not yet fully understand its normal role.

Extracts of the adenohypophysis produce a diabetic state in normal animals, and we refer to the active substance as the *diabetogenic hormone.* It inhibits the action of insulin and also diminishes the production of insulin by the pancreas. If injections are continued, the pancreas cells are injured, insulin production is reduced permanently, and thus a permanent diabetic condition is produced. The hormone unquestionably plays a role in the development of certain types of diabetes in man.

This brief review of various hormones and their functions has given a simplified picture of the condition in the living animal. Since there is a great deal of interaction between the various hormone-producing glands, as well as between the nervous system and the endocrine system, no part of the body is truly independent, and the two systems combine to carry out the integration needed in the balanced function of the organism.

HORMONES OF INVERTEBRATES

The control and integration of physiological functions in highly organized invertebrates is under the control of nerves as well as of hormones. In arthropods, annelids, and molluscs, central control lies in *large ganglia,* which are usually located in the front part of the animal and are called the *brain.* In many cases, rapid conduction from the brain to the body is assured by *giant axons.* The simple reflex has not been as completely analyzed in any invertebrate as it has been in vertebrates. The study of invertebrate neuromuscular transmission is, in general, more difficult than that in vertebrates, because one muscle is frequently supplied by many nerves that elicit different responses, but there is an advantage in that the tracts are often more accessible and the animals are more tolerant of extensive laboratory experimentation.

More primitive invertebrates, such as coelenterates, have a diffuse *nerve net* in the body wall, but they have no central ganglia that serve as controlling centers. The nerve nets are composed of nerve cells that are joined to one another by protoplasmic connections, rather than by synapses. Sponges have no definite nerve cells, but their cells are sensitive to stimulation—for example, the cells around the openings in the body wall contract if touched, and these contractions spread to nearby cells. Since the protozoans are single cells, we cannot, of course, expect to find any nervous system, but they still contain structures for coordination—for example, ciliates, such as paramecium, have a definite system of conducting fibrils, which serve to coordinate the beats of the cilia.

Endocrine function has been demonstrated in many invertebrates. Detailed knowledge of invertebrate endocrinology is restricted to a few forms, and there is room for a tremendous amount of additional research. The groups in which organs of internal secretion have been clearly demonstrated are molluscs, worms, arthropods, and tunicates. Certainly, endocrine function must exist in many other groups, and we can expect future investigations to reveal exciting information.

Two important principles are worth noting in invertebrate endocrinology: (1) In those invertebrates that have been investigated, there is an even closer connection between nervous system and endocrine function than there is in vertebrates; (2) invertebrate hormones in most aspects are entirely different from vertebrate hormones, both in chemical constitution and in function. The only vertebrate hormones that seem to have a normal role in invertebrates are acetylcholine, adrenalin, noradrenalin, and serotonin, which, characteristically, are all neurohormones. The majority of vertebrate hormones apparently do not function in invertebrates, for the injection or administration of them has little or no effect.

Endocrine function has been most thoroughly studied in crustaceans and insects. In these animals, the functions known to be influenced by hormones are reproduction, metabolic rate, molting, and growth; cells that contain pigments, the so-called chromatophores, are also affected. Further studies will undoubtedly reveal many more functions that are controlled by hormones.

Metamorphosis in Insects

In the 1930's the attention of insect physiologists became focused on the field of endocrinology, mostly because of some brilliant investigations on the South American blood-sucking bug *Rhodnius,* a relative of the bedbug. After it hatches from the egg, *Rhodnius* develops into the adult form through five nymphal stages. In each stage it must obtain a meal of blood, and some weeks after such a meal it molts by shedding the outer cuticle;

it is then ready to suck blood again in preparation for the next molt. In the last nymphal stage, the molting occurs about 28 days after the blood meal. If the animal is decapitated before a certain "critical period," which is around the seventh day, the final molting does not occur, although the animal may live for more than a year. If, however, the decapitation takes place on the eighth day or later, the animal will molt and develop into a headless adult. The molting is evidently under endocrine control, for if the blood from an insect decapitated more than 8 days after feeding is transferred into an insect decapitated before the critical period, the latter is induced to molt.

The transfusion of blood in these insects is performed by connecting them, after decapitation, by a short capillary tube fixed into the neck with paraffin. If a fifth-stage nymph that has had its blood meal and has gone through the critical period is joined in this way to one in the first stage, its blood will cause the tiny first-stage nymph, recently emerged from the egg, to develop such characteristics of the adult as wings and genital organs and thus appear as a midget adult. The hormone responsible for the development into the adult form, the *growth and differentiation hormone* (GDH), appears to be furnished by the brain, but is actually secreted by a gland in the thorax (the part that has the legs attached to it), which is stimulated to secrete GDH by another hormone that originates in the brain. The GDH is active in all molts, and without it no molt can occur.

Why is it that the first four molts give rise only to the next stage of the nymphal form and that the fifth develops into an adult? The answer lies in the action of a hormone known as the *juvenile hormone* (because it blocks the development of the mature form) which is found in the *corpus allatum,* a tiny cluster of cells just behind the brain. In the first four moltings, the presence of the juvenile hormone leads to the formation of another nymphal stage, but in the last molt the corpus allatum is inactive, the juvenile hormone is not present, and the GDH causes the adult stage to form. If the corpus allatum from a younger stage is transplanted into a fifth-stage nymph before the molting, the juvenile hormone inhibits the development of adult characters, and an artificial sixth-stage nymph, not an adult, results.

Since the GDH is necessary for each molt, but is modified by the juvenile hormone which is secreted later, simple decapitation should induce metamorphosis if the head is cut off after the brain hormone has been released, but before the juvenile hormone appears. This has proven to be the case: Decapitation of the early nymph stages, at accurately timed periods after the blood meal, has given rise to the adult type.

Even more spectacular than the work on Rhodnius have been investigations of the silkworm, the larva of a large moth. The silkworm goes through a succession of five molts and then transforms into a pupa from which, after a certain period, the adult moth emerges. In these animals it has been possible, because of their relatively large size, to remove and transplant the organs that have endocrine function, although they are scarcely visible without a microscope. If the *corpora allata* from younger larvae are transplanted into older ones, the animals fail to pupate and instead continue to grow. They can be induced to go through several extra larval molts without maturing, and thus develop into giant silkworms, several times as large as normal. If the administration of juvenile hormone is halted, however, these giants stop growing and pupate.

In the silkworm, the growth and differentiation hormone responsible for pupation is secreted by the prothoracic gland, which is located in the front of the thorax. The silkworm thus has a system of three major endocrine organs: the *corpus allatum,* which produces the juvenile hormone; the *prothoracic gland,* which yields the growth and development hormone; and the *brain,* which stimulates the prothoracic gland to hormone production. The integrated action of these organs controls the normal development through the five larval stages to the pupa, and finally to the emergence of the adult silk moth.

SELECTED READINGS

GENERAL

Carlson, A. J., and Victor Johnson, *The Machinery of the Body*. Chicago: University of Chicago Press, fifth ed., 1961. A clear, elementary text in physiology, with major emphasis on man.

Giese, A., *Cell Physiology*. Philadelphia: Saunders, second ed., 1962. An excellent text that includes the chemical and physical background necessary to understand physiology.

Harrow, Benjamin, and A. Mazur, *Textbook of Biochemistry*. Philadelphia: Saunders, eighth ed., 1962. Modern and up-to-date, avoids the technicalities of large texts.

Prosser, C. L., and F. A. Brown, Jr., *Comparative Animal Physiology*. Philadelphia: Saunders, second ed., 1961. An encyclopedic treatment of animal physiology.

SPECIAL TOPICS

Krogh, August, *The Comparative Physiology of Respiratory Mechanisms*. Philadelphia: University of Pennsylvania Press, 1959. A superb monograph on the comparative aspects of respiration.

Smith, Homer W., *From Fish to Philosopher*. Garden City, N. Y.: Doubleday, 1961. A readable account of problems of water and the role of the kidney.

Schmidt-Nielsen, Knut, *Desert Animals, Physiological Problems of Heat and Water*. Oxford: Clarendon Press, 1964. Describes how animals can live in excessive heat with little or no water.

Gray, James, *How Animals Move*. London: Cambridge University Press, 1953. A lively presentation of problems of animal motion.

Hoyle, Graham, "Comparative Physiology of the Nervous Control of Muscular Contraction," *Cambridge Monographs in Experimental Biology*, No. 8. London: Cambridge University Press, 1957. A monograph on comparative aspects of muscle physiology.

Carthy, J. D., *An Introduction to the Behavior of Invertebrates*. New York: Macmillan, 1958. Includes very useful discussions of the physiology of sensory organs.

Griffin, D. R., *Listening in the Dark*. New Haven, Conn.: Yale University Press, 1958. A book on bat sonar which proves that good biology can also be good reading.

Von Frisch, Karl, *Bees, Their Vision, Chemical Sense and Language*. Ithaca, N. Y.: Cornell University Press, 1956. A fascinating presentation by the discoverer of the language of the bees.

Sherrington, Sir Charles Scott, *Man on His Nature*. Garden City, N. Y.: Doubleday, 1953. Written by one of the masters of modern physiology, this classic study discusses the central nervous system.

Gorbman, Aubrey, and Howard A. Bern, *Textbook of Comparative Endo-crinology*. New York: Wiley, 1962. Includes hormones in lower animals, usually not thoroughly treated in other texts.

Young, J. Z., *The Life of Mammals*. New York and Oxford: Oxford University Press, 1957. Contains excellent chapters on structure and function. Chapter 1, in particular, is recommended for its discussion of the significance of information theory in biology.

Index